Andy

Thanks for the
on Arabian Oryx.
This book certainly covers
Oryx project well. And
promotes this project that you
are involved in.

Randy Riches

*Conservation and Biology
of Desert Antelopes*

Conservation and Biology of Desert Antelopes

Including the Proceedings of
The 25th Anniversary Celebration of
'Operation Oryx' Symposium

Edited by
Alexandra Dixon and David Jones

Introduction by
Sir Peter Scott, CH CBE DSC FRS

Colour photographs kindly donated by
His Majesty Sultan Qaboos bin Said, Sultan of Oman

CHRISTOPHER HELM

London

© 1988 The Zoological Society of London
Christopher Helm (Publishers) Ltd, Imperial House,
21-25 North Street, Bromley, Kent BR1 1SD

ISBN 0-7470-1604-6

A CIP catalogue record for this book
is available from the British Library

Sponsored by The Fauna and Flora Preservation Society
and The Zoological Society of London

Typeset by Florencetype Ltd, Kewstoke, Avon
Printed and bound in Great Britain
by Billing and Sons Ltd, Worcester

Contents

* Papers presented at the 'Operation Oryx' Symposium
† Posters presented at the 'Operation Oryx' Symposium

v

List of Colour Plates

Notes on Contributors

Dr Carlos L. Alados, Estacion Experimental de Zonas Aridas, Consejo Superior de Investigaciones Cientificas, General Segure 1, 04071 Almeria, Spain.

Dr Maher Z. Abu Jafer, Director General, The Royal Society for the Conservation of Nature, PO Box 6354, Amman, Jordan.

Dr Abdulaziz Abu-Zinada, Secretary-General, The National Commission for Wildlife Conservation and Development, PO Box 61681, Riyadh, Kingdom of Saudi Arabia.

Dr Brian Bertram, Curator of Mammals, The Zoological Society of London, Regents's Park, London NW1 4RY, UK.

Ms Ann Cave-Browne, c/o The Royal Zoological Society of Scotland, Edinburgh Zoo, Murrayfield, Edinburgh, EH12 6TS, UK.

Mr Ralph H. Daly, Adviser for the Conservation of the Environment, Diwan of Royal Court Affairs, PO Box 246, Muscat, Oman.

Dr Mary A. Densmore, Research Associate, Texas A and M University, College of Veterinary Medicine, Department of Veterinary Physiology and Pharmacology, College Station, Texas 77843, USA.

Ms Karen Emanuelson, c/o The Zoological Society of London, Regent's Park, London NW1 4RY, UK.

Dr Juan Escos, Estacion Experimental de Zonas Aridas, Consejo Superior de Investigaciones Cientificas, General Segure 1, 04071 Almeria, Spain.

Mr Paul Gill, Ungulate Section, The Royal Zoological Society of Scotland, Edinburgh Zoo, Murrayfield, Edinburgh EH12 6TS, UK.

Major Ian Grimwood, PO Box 45079, Nairobi, Kenya.

Dr Colin P. Groves, Department of Prehistory and Anthropology, The Australian National University, GPO Box 4, Canberra, ACT 2601, Australia.

Dr Kushal Habibi, c/o The National Commission for Wildlife Conservation and Development, PO Box 61681, Riyadh, Kingdom of Saudi Arabia.

Dr Christine M. Hawkey, Haematology, The Wellcome Laboratories, The Zoological Society of London, Regent's Park, London NW1 4RY, UK.

Ms Copelia Hays-Shahin, The Royal Society for the Conservation of Nature, PO Box 6354, Amman, Jordan.

Notes on Contributors

Mr Wayne G. Homan, Curator, Phoenix Zoo, 60 Street and E. Van Buren, PO Box 5155, Phoenix, Arizona 85010, USA.

Mr J. Kidner, c/o The Zoological Society of London, Regent's Park, London NW1 4RY, UK.

Mr Jonathan Kingdon, The Elms, Islip, Oxon OX5 2SD, UK.

Mr Steven C. Kingswood, Curator of Mammals, San Antonio Zoological Gardens and Aquarium, 3903 N St Mary's Street, San Antonio, Texas 78212, USA.

Mr Richard A. Kock, Veterinary Officer, (Whipsnade Park), The Zoological Society of London, Regent's Park, London NW1 4RY, UK.

Dr Duane C. Kraemer, Texas A and M University, College of Veterinary Medicine, Department of Veterinary Physiology and Pharmacology, College Station, Texas 77843, USA.

Ms Arlene T. Kumamoto, San Diego Zoo, Center for Reproduction of Endangered Species (CRES), PO Box 551, San Diego, California 92112, USA.

Mr David Jones, Director of Zoos, The Zoological Society of London, Regent's Park, London, NW1 4RY, UK.

Dr Georgina M. Mace, Conservation Projects Manager, National Federation of Zoos of Great Britain and Ireland, Regent's Park, London NW1 4RY, UK.

Dr Paul Munton, 9 Stanlake Villas, London W12 7EX, UK.

Mr. John Newby, World Wildlife Fund Representative, BP 10933, Niamey, Republic of Niger.

Dr Mark R. Stanley Price, Director, African Wildlife Foundation, PO Box 48177, Nairobi, Kenya. (Ex-Manager, White Oryx Project, Oman.)

Sir Peter Scott, President, The Fauna and Flora Preservation Society, 8–12 Camden High Street, London NW1 0JH, UK.

Roland Seitre, The National Commission for Wildlife Conservation and Development, PO Box 61681, Riyadh, Kingdom of Saudi Arabia.

Mr Jeremy Usher-Smith, c/o The Zoological Society of London, Regent's Park, London NW1 4RY, UK.

Dr Juan-Ramon Vericad, Estacion Experimental de Zonas Aridas, Consejo Superior de Investigaciones Cientificas, General Segure 1, 04071 Almeria, Spain.

Dr Timothy Wacher, c/o The International Trypanotolerance Centre, P.M.B. 14, Banjul, Gambia.

Dr Douglas Williamson, Research Group on Mammalian Ecology and Reproduction, Department of Physiology, Downing Street, Cambridge CB2 3EG, UK.

Ms Jane Williamson, c/o IUCN Conservation Monitoring Centre, 219c Huntingdon Road, Cambridge, CB4 0DL, UK.

Mr Michael Woodford, Apartment B708, 500 Twenty-Third Street NW, Washington, DC 20037, USA.

Acknowledgements

The success of the 25th Anniversary Celebration of 'Operation Oryx' Symposium and Banquet would not have been possible without the help of The Zoological Society of London staff, particularly the Design & Information Unit, the Gardening Department, the Catering Department and Mrs Irene Finch, David Jones's secretary. Thanks are also due to Miss Amanda Hillier at the Fauna and Flora Preservation Society. Publication of the manuscript was greatly assisted by the work of Miss Sue Anders, Mr Michael Lyster and Mr Terry Dennett of The Zoological Society of London. We thank them all.

Introduction

The Arabian Oryx *Oryx leucoryx* is once more roaming the deserts where it belongs, thanks to an international effort to ensure its survival. That it has been possible to restore this beautiful antelope to its native environment is a heartening example of what can be done if enough people are prepared to work and contribute to the long-term existence of species in the wild. We are more usually confronted with the decline of species and the relentless destruction of habitat, so the story of the Oryx is one which serves both to encourage further efforts for conservation and to illustrate the potential of what can be done when hearts and minds are united in a common purpose.

On a practical level, the Arabian Oryx has illustrated that captive-bred animals can be returned to a life in the wild. The problems which have arisen along the way—and some of them have been considerable—have been solved as a result of the resources, expertise and commitment of many individuals and institutions. In the process, a substantial amount of information has been gained and techniques have been developed with the Arabian Oryx which can be applied to other species, to ensure their continued existence.

The successful return of the Arabian Oryx has provided the focus for the development of conservation programmes in Arabia, most notably in the Sultanate of Oman, but also in Jordan and now in Saudi Arabia. As a result, there is a growing awareness of the vulnerability of desert species to hunting and to the loss of their specialised habitat, as well as a realisation that desert and sub-desert ecosystems are very fragile. For the sake of many gazelle species, Addax, Tahr and the Scimitar-horned Oryx, this awareness is most timely.

The 25th Anniversary Celebration of 'Operation Oryx' is therefore more than just a reunion of those who have been directly involved. It is an expression of appreciation for the effort and dedication that has gone into saving the Arabian Oryx from extinction. It is also an opportunity to discuss frankly how the lessons learned can be applied equally successfully to other endangered species, for, as the papers presented show, the same effort is needed now for many other desert animals of North Africa and the Middle East.

Peter Scott
Slimbridge, October 1987

*Conservation and Biology
of Desert Antelopes*

1. 'Operation Oryx':
the start of it all

Ian Grimwood

Most captive-breeding/re-introduction programmes can conveniently be divided into three stages: the collection of an adequate breeding nucleus, the building up of numbers in captivity, and the re-introduction itself. I am to try to cover the first stage with regard to the Arabian Oryx *Oryx leucoryx* programme. Before doing so, however, I should like to quote from a paper I read at the golden jubilee celebrations of the San Diego Zoo in October 1966. Having described 'Operation Oryx' up to that date, I concluded by saying, of the Arizona Zoological Society, that 'they have shown that they can breed Oryx at Phoenix and have at last shown that they can breed female Oryx too.' (The first seven calves born at Phoenix had all been males.) 'All that remains, therefore, is for them to go into mass production. We can only wish them luck in that endeavour and hope that one day we may all attend a gathering such as this to listen to a paper on how they succeeded and how the Arabian Oryx was successfully re-introduced to the wild'. I am glad that that dream has now come true.

'Operation Oryx' really began in 1961. At that time, very little was known about the status of the Arabian Oryx except that Lee Talbot, in his *A Look at Threatened Species* (1960), had reported that it appeared to be extinct in all parts of its former wide range except along the southern edge of the Rub-al-Khali. Even there the situation was so bad that he thought that the few hundred animals which might still exist would be exterminated within the next few years, and all other available evidence supported this depressing view. His recommendation of a captive-breeding programme therefore seemed to be the only way of saving the species.

Stimulated by Talbot's report, Michael Crouch, then Assistant Adviser, Northern Deserts, East Aden Protectorate, had drawn the Fauna Preservation Society's (FPS's) attention to the fact that in

April or May each year, when conditions in the sand sea itself became too hot for them, small groups of Oryx, totalling perhaps 80 to 100, were still in the habit of emerging onto the gravel plains in the northeast corner of the Protectorate, where he thought a capture attempt would be possible. This was the western end of the region indicated by Talbot. Nothing definite was known about the situation in the larger eastern part, which lay in the Sultanate of Muscat and Oman. Then, in mid-1961, Crouch reported that earlier that year a large party of hunters from Qatar had appeared in the area concerned and remained there for several weeks, during which they were known to have killed 48 Oryx. Having found this favoured spot, the hunters were bound to return. If there was to be a capture attempt it would therefore have to be made soon.

Faced with this situation, the FPS made up its mind to mount a capture operation at the first favourable opportunity, which would be in April/May 1962. As a preliminary move, Lt Col. Boyle, the Society's Secretary, who was to bear the brunt of so much correspondence over the succeeding months, obtained two most important concessions: the promise of help from the Hadharami Beduin Legion and the agreement of the Air Ministry that the Royal Air Force could assist in transport matters whenever needs coincided with routine flights. As things turned out, a capture operation would have been virtually impossible without the help of those two organisations. Meanwhile I, who had been invited to take charge of field operations and was Chief Game Warden in Kenya at the time, had been busy selecting members of the catching party, getting together stores, a catching car and spotter aeroplane, liaising with the RAF about transporting them to Aden, and in similar preparations.

A serious hitch to plans occurred in February, just a month before the advance party was due to set out, when a report was received that the hunters had returned and killed at least another 13, and possibly all, the remaining Oryx. Pessimists felt that the FPS should abandon its attempt, but the Society was by then so far committed that it decided to carry on as planned. Accordingly, the overseas members of the field party made their respective ways to Aden: Michael Woodford, the veterinary surgeon, from England; and Mick Gracie, the pilot, Don Stewart, the biologist, and Peter Whitehead, the capture expert, besides myself, from Kenya. There we met up with Michael Crouch and Tony Shepherd, our second Arabic speaker, and were later all transported to our area of operations by the Hadharami Beduin Legion—a seven days' drive from the starting point of Mukalla, which we left on 23rd April.

All that northeastern corner of the former Protectorate consists of gravel plains usually referred to as the jol', sloping gently northwards to the Rub-al-Khali or sand sea proper, which here begins in a sharp line of red dunes. Dry sandy wadis, perhaps half a mile wide, cross the jol at intervals of 10 to 15 miles and discharge into the sand sea in deltas known as ramlats. Almost all the jol is motorable, although vehicles may have difficulty in crossing some of the wadis, but it is quite impossible to drive further into the sand sea than its very fringe. The whole region is waterless except for the wells at Sanau and Habarut, which are 250 miles apart and each protected by a Hadharami Beduin Legion fort, and several years may elapse between the times when any one locality is blessed with a shower of rain. Vegetation is consequently sparse. Many of the wadis sustain a scattered growth of heather-like shrubs, which can be positively luxuriant in the ramlats. The rest of the jol, however, is bare except after rain, when small patches of Aristida grass spring up in the holllows and shallow drainage lines. These green patches persist for a season and may even provide scant dry herbage during the next year, although one often has to bend down and get the grass stems in enfilade before it is apparent.

Despite its aridity, this country supports a surprising number of resident animals in the form of small rodents, Hedgehogs *Paraechinus aethiopicus*, foxes (*Vulpes* spp.) and Arabian Gazelles *Gazella gazella cora*, and we even saw Wolves *Canis lupus* on two occasions. But the Arabian Oryx comes, or used to come, onto the jol only in the heat of the summer season, when small groups tended to congregate on any available green patches.

We set up our base camp on a wide wadi half way between Sanau and Habarut and about 10 miles back from the sand sea. There we had with us a section of the Hadharami Beduin Legion (HBL) for local protection, and a signal unit which kept us in touch with HBL desert posts and through them the outside world. Our wadi was roughly in the middle of the 150-mile front on which the Oryx traditionally emerged from the sand sea, and we could keep ourselves supplied with water and motor fuel from the two HBL forts.

Almost at the start, our portable radio beacon failed, thus reducing the usefulness of our spotter plane because the whole region is unmapped and featureless and I was always afraid of the pilot failing to find camp again. However, we had the services of two first-class trackers in the persons of Tomatum bin Harbi and Mabkhout bin Hassanah, the latter of whom had been Wilfred Thesiger's guide when he passed through this region. We therefore adopted the procedure of flying short reconnaissances over the most likely areas and then, when those failed to locate Oryx, of making ground searches of a series of defined blocks for reasonably fresh Oryx tracks. Any that were found were followed until they were obliterated or we came up with the animal that made them. The Oryx was then caught by noosing, which meant driving the catching car alongside it and slipping a noose of soft rope attached by threads to a 10-foot-long pole over its head. The rope was then broken away and the animal secured by hand, blindfolded, given a tranquiliser and crated. The actual hunting party therefore took the form of the two trackers and one of our Arabic speakers based on a HBL Landrover, with one of the trackers usually working ahead on foot, the catching car lying off to a flank, and a HBL lorry carrying the crates following as far behind as visibility would allow. Hunts usually started at 4.30 a.m. and were planned to last for two or three days, both to allow the hunting party to follow up any spoor it might be on when darkness fell and because the difficulty of tracking when the sun was at its highest shortened the working day.

It was not so difficult as might be thought for the ground search to cover the whole 150-mile front to a distance of 50 miles back from the sand sea, because in reality it meant only searching the areas of vegetation to see if an Oryx had entered or left them. We frequently came across the tracks left by the Qatari hunters' vehicles, but even months-old Oryx spoor was very uncommon. Details of our various hunts are given in an account of the whole capture attempt which was published in the December 1962 issue of *Oryx*, so I will not repeat any of them now. Suffice it to say that we gained the impression that there had been no more than 11 Oryx in the whole 8,000-square-mile area we searched. Of those, we saw and caught four, although one of them, an already wounded male, died in the process. Five had moved eastward across the Oman border, where we could not follow them, and we scared two more back into the sand sea, where capture was impossible. Thanks to the RAF, our surviving two males and single female Oryx were flown from Sanau back to Nairobi and later taken to the holding ground we had prepared for them in the arid

4

northern region near Isiolo, to await a decision on their final destination.

There was at first an unfortunate tendency to regard the capture attempt as having been successful, because we had managed to catch three Oryx when the whole Aden Protectorate population had reportedly been wiped out, and in the process justified FPS's decision to carry on with the operation. The fact could not, however, be ignored that two males and one female did not constitute the viable breeding nucleus we had set out to obtain. A search was therefore begun for other Oryx already in captivity which could be added to the three we had caught to help retrieve the situation.

The Zoological Society of London was known to be willing to make available the healthy young female it owned, but the resulting two pairs would still be too small a nucleus to rely on. All the other Arabian Oryx claimed or reported to be held in western zoos turned out on investigation to be Addax *Addax nasomaculatus*, Scimitar-horned Oryx *Oryx dammah* or hybrids. It therefore became clear that the only way of building up a satisfactory nucleus without the uncertainties and expense of a second capture attempt would be to obtain some of the Oryx that the catching party had heard reports of in private hands in Arabia. Those amounted to two animals of unknown sex reported as seen wandering in the souqs of Taiz in Yemen, two females owned by HH Sheikh Jaber Abdullah al-Sabah of Kuwait, and a group of at least eight kept by HM King Saud bin Abdul Aziz at his palace in Riyadh.

Meanwhile, a location for the breeding attempt itself had been decided upon. Although Oryx could probably be bred under normal zoo conditions almost anywhere in the world, it was thought that they should be given the benefit of the climate they were used to, if only to condition them for any subsequent re-introduction move. The desert region of southwest USA was therefore looked on with favour. Accordingly, when Mr Maurice Machris, the then President of the Shikar Safari Club, put forward a joint proposal with the Arizona Zoological Society whereby the Shikar Safari Club would 'adopt' the Arabian Oryx project and pay for the establishment and maintenance of the breeding herd at Phoenix Zoo, the offer was gratefully accepted by all concerned. In addition to providing any extra facilities needed at Phoenix and the cost of transporting the Isiolo and London Oryx there, the offer included the cost of acquiring and transporting any other animals that could be obtained, or, if need be, paying the expenses of a second capture attempt. This was not only exceedingly generous but it also solved the problem of how to pay for any animals we might solicit, because funds from other sources were beginning to run low.

As a first step, the Oryx we had captured were flown from Isiolo to the Clifton quarantine station in New York in May 1963, being joined en route by the female from London Zoo. This move was facilitated by the US Department of Agriculture's agreeing, after inspecting the Isiolo holding ground, to accept the time the Oryx had spent there as the period for which they would otherwise have had to be held at an approved quarantine station such as those at Naples, Mombasa or Hamburg. We had taken the precaution of siting it on a Kenya internal cattle quarantine area and of bull-dozing off the surface of the land before building the pens. These latter were surrounded by a double fence and palisade 11 feet high to ward off attacks by Lions *Panthera leo* or Leopards *P. pardus* (which three times attempted to break in), while an intermediate channel filled with Coppertox guarded against the more deadly threat from ticks, which are the vectors of so many fatal diseases in Africa. Nevertheless, we in Kenya were very relieved to see the Oryx depart unharmed.

While all this was going on, attempts to contact the private owners of Oryx in Arabia had been progressing slowly. It was Tony Shepherd who gained the first success when, in March 1963, he managed through friends to get a letter explaining the situation into the hands of HH Sheikh Jaber Abdullah al-Sabah of Kuwait himself. That gentleman reacted in an altogether exemplary manner by immediately offering to present both the Oryx he owned to the World Herd, as we had begun to call it, and by repudiating the need for the African animals he had been offered in exchange. He also offered any other help he could give in the future. Unfortunately, one of his animals died before arrange-ments for collection could be made, but the other one was brought to Mombasa, again with RAF help, and, after spending the statutory period in the quarantine station there, was flown to Clifton in August 1963. The World Herd now totalled two males and three females.

Contacting HM King Saud of Saudi Arabia proved to be more difficult. He was a sick man at the time and spent much of the year under treatment out of the country. Numerous approaches at different levels to other members of the royal family brought no response, and it was not until July 1963 that Mr Sherman Haight of New York, who was a personal friend of the King's, received a message through the Ambassador that His Majesty would be pleased to present two pairs of his Oryx to the World Herd. Collecting those animals also turned out to be difficult, one of the obstacles being that only *Saudi Air* could use the Riyadh airport and that airline was not prepared to carry animals. However, after months of correspondence with HH Prince Fadh al Faisal, who was handling matters from the Saudi Arabian end, and with and between Maurice Machris and WWF-US who were going to share the cost with the Shikar Safari Club, and other participants, all difficulties were eventually overcome. Nevertheless, it was not until March 1964 that the way was clear for me to go to Riyadh to collect the animals and escort them by chartered flight to Beirut and on by *Pan Am* freight to Naples, where Dr Cuneo of the Naples Zoo and quarantine station had offered to quarantine them free of charge as a contribution to 'Operation Oryx'. From there they were flown to Clifton in June and eventually reached Phoenix at the end of July, to bring the total of the World Herd up to, not nine, but 11, because two calves had already been born there.

Initial approaches to the Taiz authorities had met with a refusal to part with the two Oryx reported there, which turned out to be the property of the municipal zoo. Nothing had been learnt about their ages or sex, but they were known to be hornless and were said to be in poor condition when last seen. The four male and five female adults at Phoenix had already proved their ability to breed freely and appeared to be an adequate, if perhaps marginal, number from which to build up a captive population. It was therefore decided, for the time being at least, not to make any further attempts to obtain the Taiz animals or to seach for other sources from which the World Herd could be augmented.

There was also the comforting knowledge that the Phoenix group was no longer the only potential breeding group known to exist in captivity. A further six males and three females, healthy and well cared for animals, had remained at Riyadh after the two pairs left for Phoenix. That group, however, did not remain intact for long because shortly afterwards a professional dealer obtained a pair of them, it was said in exchange for two young Orang-utans *Pongo pygmaeus*. As a matter of interest, it was from that single pair that the Los Angeles Zoo group descended, and furthermore produced a succession of female calves while the Phoenix animals seemed unable to produce anything but males.

Before handing over to Mr Homan to carry on the story, I should like to draw attention to how appropriate the carelessly given title of World Herd turned out to be. In the end, it took three years of continuous effort for the FPS to realise its original intention of establishing a captive breeding nucleus of Arabian Oryx, and before that end had been achieved no fewer than six governments or heads of state had become involved, including units of the armed forces of three of them—the RAF, the Hadharami Beduin Legion and later the Arizona Air National Guard. In addition, five zoos and a score of societies, government and international agencies, and major commercial organisations had all played significant parts, as had literally hundreds of individuals in Arabia, Africa, Europe and the USA. This is unfortunately not the place to acknowledge their individual contributions, but I cannot end without paying tribute to Lt Col. Boyle, the Society's Secretary, for his skill in co-ordinating it all.

References

Talbot, L.M. (1960) *A Look at Threatened Species*. Fauna Preservation Society, London.

2. The Establishment of the World Herd

Wayne G. Homan

Our affiliation with the Arabian Oryx *Oryx leucoryx* project started 24 years ago. At that time, Phoenix Zoo was a young institution and its association with a new and innovative conservation project presented great opportunities, beginning with the arrival of four Arabian Oryx at Phoenix Airport on the afternoon of 25 June 1963. The group had already successfully completed a 30-day stay in the Government's quarantine station and contained the three animals Major Grimwood caught in Aden and the female 'Caroline' entrusted to the project by London Zoo. Two-and-a-half months later, a lone female arrived in Phoenix as a gift to the project from the Sultan of Kuwait, HH Sheikh Jaber Abdullah al-Sabah.

Anxiety prevailed during these early days, for there were few precedents for the captive husbandry of Arabian Oryx. So little was known that even the gestation period was a mystery. We proceeded cautiously. Oryx personnel were restricted from contact with other zoo ruminants to prevent cross-contamination. Antiseptic foot baths were stationed at each entrance to the double-fenced compound. Tools and food-containers were sterilised before each use. Water was carefully measured and rationed for fear of causing illness owing to over-drinking.

The 23rd of October 1963 was the red-letter day for the project. Four months after her arrival, the female 'Edith' gave birth to the herd's first calf. Although conception had occurred during the animals' quarantine in Kenya, it did not deter the celebration, especially for the news media. This was the completion of the second step in the three-step programme: (1) *rescue* the remaining Oryx and place them in a secure environment where (2) they could be *bred* in numbers until such time as the captive population could offer surplus for (3) *restocking the wild*. So much publicity was given to this birth that it led one wag to entitle his report 'The herd that was shot around the world'.

9

Further additions were made in the following spring with a second birth. This time the mating had taken place at the Phoenix Zoo, so we were able, for the first time, to record the exact gestation period: 260 days. More good news that spring came when the project's founders were able to announce the acquisition of two new pairs of Oryx. These animals were from the stock of eight males and five females at Riyadh Zoo and were a gift to the project by HH King Saud bin Abdul Aziz of Saudi Arabia. These proved to be the last animals imported by the project and therefore the following seven animals (Table 2.1) were known as 'World Herd Founders'.

Table 2.1: Arabian Oryx World Herd Founders

Males	'Tomatum' and 'Pat'	Wild-caught
Male	'Riyadh'	Riyadh Zoo stock
Female	'Edith'	Wild-caught
Female	'Caroline'	London Zoo stock (wild-caught)
Females	'Cuneo' and 'Lucy'	Riyadh Zoo stock

Note: The female 'Salwa' from Kuwait and the male 'Aziz Aziz' from Riyadh Zoo stock were non-reproductive and do not qualify as founders.

A later infusion of new blood occurred when Phoenix and the Los Angeles Zoo exchanged animals, Los Angeles having received a pair of the remaining Riyadh Zoo animals in 1967. This brought the total American continent founders to nine, a small assemblage which represented the whole gene pool for the project's future population.

Because the premiss of the programme was to return stock to the original habitat, we needed to ensure that we would be returning the 'same' animal to the wild, one in which successful survival adaptations were preserved and with little or no domestic traits. To do this, we had to maximise the genetic sampling with each generation. The programme consisted of selectively pairing individuals to produce the greatest distribution of blood lines. Each cow was bred and allowed to produce a calf from each bull. The calves were then bred back to each unrelated founder and to other unrelated calves.

One of our primary goals was to ensure the survival and vigorous start to life of each calf. Pregnant cows were placed in semi-isolation 30 days prior to parturition and maintained there for an additional 30 days before rejoining the herd. Not only did this programme develop healthy, vigorous calves which were destined to become breeding stock, but it served to prolong the breeding potential of the founder cows by prohibiting breeding during the post-partum heat, thereby thwarting early burn-out. As an example, the founder 'Edith' from the Aden expedition lived 16 years at Phoenix and produced 13 calves.

Facilities for the animals consisted of four holding pens 15 × 65 metres and two herd-breeding pens 75 × 75 metres. In 1970, a maternity complex was constructed adjacent to the breeding pens to combat the threat of early 'navel ill' in the newborn calves. This unit consisted of five small outdoor pens each connected to a covered stall. Both indoor and outdoor areas were sanitised after each use and allowed to stand vacant for 30 days before re-use.

The herd's birth rate began an upward spiral and in 1972, with the inventory at 35, the trustees elected to transfer six animals to the San Diego Zoo. This accomplished two goals: most importantly, with the herd distributed in two separate locations some 400 miles apart, it reduced the possibility of an epidemic disease wiping out the entire herd; secondly, it relieved the crowding at Phoenix. Births continued at an ever-increasing rate, and by 1976 Phoenix again spun off surplus. This time, eight animals went to San Diego and four were sent to the zoo at Brownsville, Texas, to establish yet another breeding centre. By the time the first issue of the Arabian Oryx studbook was published in 1977, there were 106 animals on the North American continent listed, 72 of which comprised the World Herd. The remaining 34 animals were owned by the Los Angeles Zoo.

The growth rate of any group of higher organisms depends on the number of females capable of having offspring. Unfortunately, 'Operation Oryx's' first four years of calf production produced seven males, thereby limiting the calf production to the four founder females for the first seven years of the project's existence. Eventually, this calf sex bias was overcome and by 1978 it was possible to return the first animals to the Middle East. San Diego Zoo sent four male Oryx to the newly completed Shaumari Reserve in Jordan. Two years later, three Phoenix females, along with a fourth bred at San Diego, joined these bachelors. Another

11

Middle Eastern shipment occurred that same year when Los Angeles Zoo sent four pairs of animals to Hai-Bar Game Reserve in Israel.

The trustees of the World Herd decided in 1979 to disperse part of the herd to the European continent. In compliance, the Phoenix Zoo sent animals to Berlin, Antwerp and Zurich Zoos and two additional pairs were transported to San Diego. The understanding with the European zoos receiving these animals was that, when a number equal to their original stock was bred, the new animals would go to London. This would disperse the herd to an even greater extent, thereby increasing the safety margin.

The year 1981 saw the completion of the third and final portion of the project, when San Diego Zoo made the first shipment of Arabian Oryx to Oman. By 1982, these animals were acclimatised and released into the wild. This, then, completed the aims of the project, and in August 1982 an agreement was circulated among the trustees which formally dissolved 'Operation Oryx'. The dissolution document made two stipulations upon its members to ensure the continuation of the project's aims. The first was that the Zoological Society of San Diego maintain a reservoir of female Arabian Oryx, the progeny of which would be introduced into the native habitat. The second was that all zoos who were members of the project would co-operate with the International Union for Conservation of Nature and Natural Resources (IUCN) and the World Wildlife Fund in providing Arabian Oryx for future distribution into the wild at no charge.

The contribution of zoos to the return of the Arabian Oryx is likely to continue and the future is promising. The American Association of Zoological Parks and Aquariums (AAZPA), which represents virtually every major professionally operated zoological park and aquarium on the continent, has nominated the Arabian Oryx for Species Survival Plan status. This means that member institutions holding the species have been invited to sign a 'Memorandum of Participation' in a programme of population management. The group met for the first time on 30 March 1987. Eight institutions participated and had a total Oryx inventory of 190 animals. There was considerable discussion concerning the addition of animals to the release programme in Oman and it was agreed that this would be done on a yearly basis. Nine animals were listed as candidates for shipment in this year.

'Operation Oryx' has been a success in more ways than in saving the Arabian Oryx. It is a positive demonstration that the zoo community can be relied upon for aid in the sustainment of endangered species, and it provides proof that the re-introduction of a species extinct in the wild is a viable possibility.

3. The Early Stages of Re-introduction of the Arabian Oryx in Oman

Ralph H. Daly

Although I was a Political Officer in the Western Aden Protectorate when Ian Grimwood brought his task force for 'Operation Oryx' into the Eastern Aden Protectorate in 1962, I was only remotely aware of what they were doing. It was not until 1972 when I heard that the last Oryx had been killed by raiders from abroad that 'Operation Oryx' came back to mind, and it was a further two years before I became directly involved.

In 1974, I was appointed Adviser for Conservation of the Environment in Oman. It was soon apparent that HM The Sultan was keenly interested in establishing programmes whereby the native fauna and flora of this country could be studied and protected as part of Oman's national heritage. Initially, our attention was focused on Arabian Tahr *Hemitragus jayakari* and marine turtles (Chelonidae), but Oryx were quickly added to the list. In this way it was possible to begin to fulfil the ultimate objective of 'Operation Oryx': the return of the species to the wild.

The likely co-operation of the Harasis tribesmen in protecting the Oryx and the availability of suitable habitat were major assets in the development of the project, but the great uncertainty remained of whether Oryx, bred for several generations in zoos, would survive in the desert on their own. Luckily, the dedication of His Majesty to the return of the Oryx and his willingness to provide funds for capital and recurrent expenditure, combined with careful planning and hard work, have made it possible for Dr Mark Stanley Price and me to be with you here today, telling you how the dream came true and prospers as a continuing reality in the central desert of Oman.

Although the project to return Oryx to the wild immediately received the complete support of the Sultan, it was clear that, before any animals could be re-introduced, a study of the proposed sites was absolutely necessary. There were very few facts about the life and habits of the Arabian Oryx *Oryx leucoryx* in the wild to go on, and no studies had ever been made of the ecology of the central desert of Oman. It was assumed that the species had disappeared from its range because of over-hunting, but there may have been other reasons such as destruction of habitat or climatic changes. We therefore decided that a feasibility study must be carried out to cover the following: (i) to establish as far as possible the basic ecological requirements of the Arabian Oryx; (ii) to review the natural history and the human use of the re-introduction area; (iii) to determine if the area would satisfy the requirements of the species; (iv) to propose a re-introduction strategy and technique.

Looking back now over the past 11 years in the light of all we have learned about the Oryx, the ecology of the area and the people who inhabit it—the Harasis themselves—I am rather appalled at our temerity. However, we had some bold and know-ledgeable people to help with the field work: Dr Ray Lawton from the Land Resources Development Centre of the then British Ministry of Overseas Development studied the vegetation; Dr Michael Woodford, wildlife veterinarian on Major Grimwood's 'Operation Oryx' team, helped with his wide knowledge of the behaviour of wild ungulates in their natural habitats; Major Michael Gallagher, ornithologist and all-round naturalist with an extensive knowledge of the flora and fauna of southern Arabia, and, very importantly, Ibrahim bin Saqqar al-Harsusi, an old friend of mine from my oil company days, guided us unerringly about the enormous and largely trackless area from Oman's frontier with South Yemen in the west to the foothills of the Hajjar mountains in the north.

I also owe a great debt of gratitude for their enthusiastic help, encouragement and sound advice to Sir Peter Scott, who was then Chairman of the Survival Service Commission, to his deputy, Dr Wayne King, and to Mr Richard Fitter of the Fauna Preservation Society, as it was then. I should also like to take the opportunity of thanking Dr Jim Dolan and his staff at the San Diego Wild Animal Park for coping with our demanding animal health requirements and for arranging the despatch of the Oryx to Oman (I am glad to tell you that he has recently agreed to do it all over again!).

In discussions with the sheikhs and other influential representatives of all the sections of the Harasis, it was soon apparent that the tribe was extremely interested in the idea of re-introducing the

15

Oryx into the wild on the Jidda'. To begin with, however, most of the tribesmen were worried that the animals which we proposed to bring from the USA were not really the same kind of Oryx that they used to know. Some found it hard to believe that the American animals, even if they really were descendants of their *'Bin Sola'*, would be able to breed and live off the land in the wild. A few remained quietly sceptical about the kind of Oryx we would produce until they beheld them with their own eyes on that never-to-be-forgotten day when the first Oryx stepped out of their crates into the pens at Yalooni on 10 March 1980. For the old men it was a return of a well-known part of the past; for the younger ones it was the materialisation of a mythical element of their cultural history. From that day onwards, the Oryx project with its centre at Yalooni started to become an integral part of the life and economy of the Harasis, and the Yalooni camp developed as a desert research centre.

In the beginning, there was a divergence of opinion concerning the proposed re-introduction strategy and technique. Some recommended starting with a small number of males and releasing them as a bachelor herd. Those with experience of wild Oryx herds in Africa, however, recommended the pre-integration approach and certainly after listening to Michael Woodford, and later Mark Stanley Price himself, I was convinced that this was the right way to achieve our aim of establishing a viable herd of Oryx in the wild. This approach, of course, took time; the animals of different ages and sexes for the first herd arrived in three widely separated lots from America as zoo-bred animals. It took two years to integrate them fully in our 1-km^2 enclosure.

I shall shortly hand over the rostrum to Mark Stanley Price to tell you about the field operations and research work at Yalooni. Mark came to us as Field Manager for the project from Africa, where he was taking Fringe-eared Oryx *Oryx gazella calotis* from the wild to turn them into herds of domestic livestock. His aim in Oman was to take zoo-bred Arabian Oryx from America and turn them into herds of wild animals to live and thrive in the desert of their homeland. After almost eight years, he has left us to return to Africa, leaving behind 34 Arabian Oryx living on the Jidda' among its other wild creatures and the Harasis beduin, just as their ancestors did long ago.

For the future, we aim to increase the number of Oryx success-fully breeding in the wild as fast as possible on as good a genetic

16

basis as we can manage. In the last four months, we have had three good calves born unseen in the wild without trouble. From recent observations it seems certain that two of these calves are females. The Royal Society for the Conservation of Nature in Jordan has very kindly agreed to give us two males and two females, of the age groups we most need, from its herd of about 70 animals at Shaumari and we expect to receive them at Yalooni in the early autumn. The North American Oryx breeders, through their Species Survival Plan Committee under the Chairmanship of Dr Jim Dolan, have agreed to send Oman a regular—annual if possible—supply of Oryx, and before the end of this year we hope to receive the first consignment of eight or ten animals, chosen for their genetic compatibility with our proven good desert-breeding Oryx.

Only when we have 200 or 300 wild Oryx, roaming freely in the central desert of Oman, shall we be able to say with confidence to HM Sultan Qaboos bin Said and the world: 'Operation Oryx' successfully completed.

4 Field Operations and Research in Oman

Mark R. Stanley Price

Introduction

The Arabian Oryx *Oryx leucoryx* re-introduction area lies in central Oman and comprises the area known at the start of 'Operation Oryx' to contain the last viable population of the species. The last of these Oryx were killed or captured here in 1972 (Henderson, 1974), but their recent presence was a significant factor in selection of the area (Jungius, 1985).

The re-introduction area spans the 20°N line of latitude and is a distinct ecological and geomorphological unit called the Jiddat-al-Harasis. The Jidda' is a plateau about 150 metres above sea level of Miocene limestone overlain by shallow, wind-blown sand and a variety of stony pavement surfaces. As the limestone surface has been subject to little erosion or deposition, there is only a poorly developed surface-drainage pattern. Water runs off into scattered solution hollows in which it rarely stands for more than a short time because of the occurrence of sink-holes, although these are often choked with sand. The Jidda's eastern limit is the Huqf escarpment, at the foot of which there are low-yielding seepages of very brackish water. The Jidda' itself has no natural water sources.

The re-introduction site is at Yalooni, the largest such pan on the Jidda', where the vegetation is relatively diverse. Lying in the central Jidda', the camp is approximately equidistant from the Arabian Sea and the southern edge of the sand seas of the Rub-al-Khali. The climate is typical in many ways of continental deserts in both its daily and its seasonal variation in humidity and temperature. The temperature on the hottest June day is 47°C in the shade, while the average January maximum is 26°C with extreme records of 7°C. Every day air temperature varies by 15–20°C. Rainfall at Yalooni averaged 52 millimetres from 1980 to 1986, with a spread of between 0 and 200 millimetres. Despite this low rainfall, the vegetation is well developed and characterised by abundant trees of *Acacia tortilis*, *A. ehrenbergiana* and *Prosopis cineraria*. The most dependable source of moisture for the vegetation is the fogs which roll in from the Arabian Sea, most commonly in spring and autumn. Their water is equivalent to an annual 18 litres/square metre of surface area of an artificial collecting surface. Consequently, vegetation responds with two growing seasons when air temperatures are moderate and water is available.

These peculiar ecological conditions allowed the Harasis bedu to practise a nomadic subsistence pastoralism which was highly specialised even by the standards of Arabia. Through careful exploitation of their environment, their livestock were independent of drinking water for months at a time while the families and their flocks were highly mobile, utilising the low level of primary production produced by fog moisture. Human water requirements were met by collecting the droplets of condensed fog moisture from tree canopies. This ecosystem also supported a diverse wildlife fauna, of which the Oryx was the largest herbivore, but the Arabian Gazelle *Gazella gazella cora* was the most numerous (the area still supports the largest population of this gazelle in Arabia). All wildlife is protected from hunting by a law which pre-dates the re-introduction of the Oryx.

Management Strategy for Re-introduction

In preparation for living in the desert, Oryx management was based on seven principles:

1. The imported Oryx should be fully acclimatised to the more rigorous desert climate.

2. They should be habituated to the sights, smells and sounds of their new environment with its people, animals, vehicles.

3. Comparative observations show all Oryx species to be gregarious. Therefore, the basic unit for release should be a herd which simulated the ancestral type. In essence, this 'integrated' herd would total no fewer than ten individuals, with approximately equal numbers of each sex, which would have been together long enough for a stable hierarchy to have developed.

4. The Oryx should be conditioned to develop a fidelity to the

release area, around which their home range would develop. Conversely, if the Oryx were determined to flee the release area when free, it would negate its careful selection as suitable habitat during the feasibility study. This conditioning was done through supplementary feeding and, more importantly, the provision of water.

5. To minimise the stress and demands on the Oryx on taking up free life in the desert, the transition from captivity to the open desert should be as smooth as possible. This affects the season of release and the actual process.

6. In addition to these aspects of Oryx management, it was obvious that the released Oryx had to be guarded to prevent any repetition of the slaughter which caused the original extinction. By employing the local people as wildlife rangers, the project would provide good employment in a very remote area. On the other hand, the re-introduction area is so large that no amount of patrolling could ensure effective protection for free-ranging Oryx in the face of a malevolent local population. Therefore, project management has had to ensure that the formal benefits of employment are spread evenly through the tribe and the project camp has become an

Table 4.1: Research and monitoring observations on wild Oryx

Opportunistically
1. Behavioural: activity, dominance, leadership, separations
2. Feeding records
3. Size and condition
4. Sexual activity
5. Isolation of mother and newborn calf

Daily
1. Herd location
2. Identification and location of any separated
3. Times into and out of shade
4. Location and surveillance of lying-out calves
5. Amounts of feed and water

At intervals
1. Faecal nitrogen level
2. Diet nitrogen level
3. Faecal parasite ova check

---

integral part of local community life. It has been able to do this by providing minor services or assistance, or helping with communications, at very little financial cost to itself within the framework of a mutually agreed set of rules and limits.

7. Finally, in view of the step into the unknown which the re-introduction represented, it was agreed that as much information as was feasible should be gathered on Oryx behaviour and performance from their arrival in Oman and then for as long as possible after release. The main types of observation are shown in Table 4.1. It is clear that many of these observations relied on the rangers, who were near the animals for security reasons. This data-collection role provides added motivation and interest for the rangers.

Provision of Oryx

In 1979, the World Herd trustees agreed to provide Oman in 1980 with 12 Oryx with a sex ratio of 6:6. Oman requested a range of ages within each sex and at least one female with breeding experience. It was also felt desirable that the twelve should have run together in the USA so that any unsuitable individuals could be substituted.

This integration of the herd was not possible at San Diego Wild Animal Park, and then, shortly before shipping, seven out of the twelve Oryx earmarked for Oman were positive for Blue-tongue virus, despite showing no clinical signs. Thus, Oryx arrived in Oman in batches as available and meeting Oman's veterinary requirements. The third consignment contained two extra unsoli-cited males, one of moderate age, which caused social problems in Oman. Because of this biased sex ratio and the apparent viability of the first herd in the wild, three more females were requested to promote a second herd. With their arrival, Oman had received a total of 17 animals from the USA and a young male was later donated by the Jordanian Royal Society for the Conservation of Nature.

Preparation for Release

Oryx arrived in Oman after between 45 and 90 hours in individual crates, which caused no problems of water stress. They were released into one or both of two 20 metre × 20 metre pens in a combination largely on the advice of the accompanying keeper, who was familiar with the animals. One animal was highly excitable and was kept in the pens for only two days, but most spent two to seven months inside, the upper limit depending on the composition of Oryx already in the enclosure.

The enclosure led from the pens and covered 1 km² of natural vegetation of several types. Here herd development took place, with the enclosure's size allowing escape for an animal after any initial fighting on being added to the group. It also provided the opportunity to observe Oryx behaviour under almost natural conditions and for everyone to familiarise himself/herself with the animals and their individual behaviour. Hay and lucerne supplemented the grazing as necessary, and water was available every night, allowing measurement of consumption. No attempt was made to reduce water dependency in the enclosure.

Table 4.2: Composition of Herds 1 and 2 at release

	Herd 1 (released 31/1/82)		Herd 2 (released 4/4/84)	
	Name	Age (months)	Name	Age (months)
Males	Jadib	45	Lubtar	80
	Nafis	41	Mustafan	68
	Museba	35	Khalifa	14
	Hamid	33	Sulayman*	5
Females	Salama	43	Farida	74
	Talama	34	Selma	47
	Rahaima	34	Zeena	27
	Hadya	29	Hababa	23
	Selma*	21	Mundassa*	22
	Alaga*	8	Kateeba*	14
			Mafrooda*	12

* = born in enclosure

The periods spent in the enclosure varied between two and 24 months depending on circumstances. A herd was judged ready for release when monitoring of the rates and types of interaction between individuals showed a low frequency of mild interactions only, with an unambiguous dominance hierarchy, and the herd moved around the enclosure as a unit with the dominant male herding and marking by squat-defaecating. Release was avoided in the hottest months because of the greater danger of heat stress following running, and was also scheduled for periods when the grazing around the enclosure was indifferent, thereby discouraging dispersal. A smooth release was obtained by moving the feed troughs from inside to just outside the gate.

Details of the two herds developed in this way and those released are shown in Table 4.2. 'Selma' was released twice because, as the first calf born in Oman and then hand-reared, she was too imprinted on the author to follow Herd 1 all the time. She was mated in the wild, then returned to the enclosure, where she had two calves before being released with Herd 2, since when she has been a normal Oryx.

Monitoring after Release

Outside the enclosure, the task of monitoring the Oryx and ensuring their security is the responsibility of the Harasis rangers. When a herd is away from the immediate vicinity of Yalooni, a patrol consists of two rangers in a vehicle with HF radio communication and fully equipped for three days and nights in the field. Oryx in each herd were released with radio collars and all the rangers were able to use the receiving equipment efficiently, being pre-trained with a radio-collared Camel.

The patrol's main task is to locate its herd, or all component Oryx of it, each morning and to radio back a report. A spare patrol is always ready on stand-by in camp to go to help if, for example, a herd has made a major move overnight. Moves of 45 kilometres are common. Co-ordination and direction of the patrols is done over the radio by the Head Ranger or Manager. These arrangements ensured that until at least mid-1986 the location of almost every Oryx was known every day.

How do Wild Oryx Respond to and Exploit their Environment?

Monitoring the released Oryx of both herds has yielded a wide range of diverse observations which basically demonstrate the Oryx's ability to survive again on the Jiddat-al-Harasis.

1. Home Range Development

Considering only Herd 1 after just over four years in the wild, the herd had a total range of 2,000 km^2 and, with rain since mid-1986, this is now probably nearer 3,000 km². The total range is composed of a series of distinct and disconnected ranges (Figure 4.1). The periods of occupancy of each varied from one to 18 months, the latter occurring when the herd returned to the release site during the very dry conditions after being away from it for 22 months. The range areas varied between 35 km² and 365 km², but ten out of 12 had areas of 100–300 km². These give Oryx densities of one Oryx per 24–31 km².

Figure 4.1: Herd 1 range development

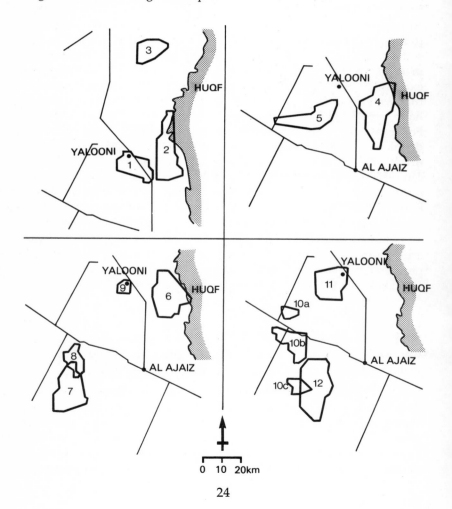

The moves between ranges into new country are in response to rain. Analysis of Yalooni wind data shows that Oryx move into an area of recent rainfall once wind direction has veered so that the herd is directly downwind of this area. Range changes without rain are usually returns to previously used areas. Exploration and range extension occur to significant extents only after rain, so that the pattern of rainfall over time and space, and the distance over which it can be detected, markedly affect the rate of Oryx independence and also account for the uneven pattern of use around the release site.

2. Water Relations

After good rain, water stands on the Jiddat-al-Harasis for only two to three weeks except at exceptional sites, which tend to be heavily settled with bedu. Water has never been taken to wild Oryx; this is in order to avoid their returning to the same site in the future expecting to find water there, and also to reinforce their knowledge that water is always available only at Yalooni. On occasion, Oryx have left their herd to walk long distances into Yalooni to drink. For example, a seven-months-pregnant female, who had last drunk 9½ months previously, returned 45 kilometres overnight to drink; she drank 11 litres and returned to the herd at once. Oryx can easily drink 15% of their body weight, and this rises to 20% under more extreme conditions. Such instances confirm that the Oryx know water is available at the release site and that they are capable of assessing the costs and benefits of a long round trip to drink.

As most of the Oryx range has no standing water, the animals are clearly water-independent in the conventional sense for long periods of time. Even without standing water, however, water is available from two obvious sources:

(a) Food: if their food grasses contain 50% moisture, the Oryx can be water-independent even in summer temperatures of 40°C. If the temperature drops to 31°C, 35% moisture is adequate. The herd was seen to leave an area when the grass contained only 35% water and the ambient shade temperature was 42.5°C.

(b) Condensed water: considerable volumes of water are available as dew and particularly as fog moisture at certain times of the year. This source drives the two growing seasons each year, even in the absence of rain. Heavy fog stimulates grazing and the Oryx may even lick stones and have been seen to lick one another. There is evidence that the desert grasses are hygroscopic on damp nights.

The Oryx's water-independence is obviously enhanced by techniques of water-loss avoidance, of which only some are apparent through observation alone. As air temperature rises above 29–30°C, shading time increases, thereby lowering the water need for evaporative cooling. Water balance is also facilitated by the seasonal changes in coat colour and density which aid maintenance of thermal equilibrium through the year. Finally, when water-independent in hot months, Oryx urinate less and the faecal moisture content decreases by 20%.

3. Behaviour and Environmental Perception

Some indication of the way in which the behaviour of re-introduced Oryx promotes successful existence in the desert is shown in two aspects, namely their behaviour when accidentally separated from the herd and, secondly, their ability to navigate and recall places.

Oryx are rarely separated accidentally from their herd (see below). As the herd grazes by day, ten animals may be spread over an area of 1 km², but each is vigilant and attempts to maintain visual contact with at least one fellow. Subordinate males have been seen to move deliberately to take up a position between the body of the herd and outlying females, providing the latter with a chain of visual contact. If an Oryx finds itself alone, it runs to a nearby rise and scans, and will usually find the herd. Most accidental separations occur at night, on a small scale if the arrival of fog has stimulated activity, but many large moves between ranges also occur at night. In the morning, the separated animal searches the currently used area for the herd and examines tracks. Occasionally, Oryx have been watched tracking the herd up. If the herd is not found in this area, the animal stands motionless on a rise, exploiting its whiteness to advertise itself. If this fails to locate the herd, the Oryx settles down to live alone in the same range area. If the herd has merely gone on an exploratory foray of a day or two, it will return to the area. If this has not happened after a few days, the separated animal may leave and start to revisit the areas previously used by the herd. As neither party will have moved into a new range in the absence of rain, these techniques virtually ensure a reunion in a reasonable period despite the large distances involved. Although it seems that each Oryx has to experience for itself living alone without panic, this behaviour has the important management consequence that it is not necessary for a patrol to devote its efforts to monitoring one separated animal.

Former ranges are visited after intervals of months or years. The precision with which a herd heads, for example, for a heap of Camel bones which it last chewed long ago indicates the accuracy with which areas once occupied are remembered. Similarly, individuals or groups return to Yalooni for water, locating the point water source in a direct heading on a moonless night.

When moving between two familiar areas through relatively unused country, a herd may take the same line, or a Camel or car track, repeatedly. The Oryx may gain more information from other Oryx tracks if many use the same route. Locating travelling Oryx is also helped because tracks may be intercepted by checking on such favoured routes. When on the move, Oryx are constantly integrating information on heading and distance and use this awareness of their relative location at all times: for example, to make a 60-kilometre trek through new territory from one range to another familiar area. A few observations show that this ability to navigate and remember sites is well developed in desert-born juvenile Oryx.

Selective Pressures during Re-introduction

The eighteen original immigrant Oryx represented a nearly random genetic selection of those in captivity in the USA and Jordan. It would be clearly unrealistic to expect all both to be fit for release into the wild and to perform equally well there. This influences the policy towards intervening to provide veterinary treatment in order to allow the survival of an animal which is likely to die if faced with some other natural challenge. On the other hand, careful monitoring of performance and analysis of causes of death have yielded some conclusions relevant to the selection of further immigrants and for the re-introduction of captive-bred animals in general.

Two of the eighteen immigrants showed behaviour in the pens which suggested their unsuitability for release. An elderly male paced continuously as a result of a long period in a zoo pen, while a young female had been in an exhibit pen and showed a strong attraction to people. Such obviously unsuitable traits should have resulted in substitution while still in the USA, for they reduced the effective number of immigrants to 16.

Of the 9:9 immigrants, 4:4 had died by mid-1987 after periods in

Oman ranging between one month (death due to snake bite) and 66 months, of which 53 were spent in the wild. The causes of death in the eight were varied, with bacterial infection often playing a primary or secondary role. The presence of *Clostridium botulinum* was the only common factor in two deaths and both females were known scavengers, with poor breeding records.

Six immigrant females had produced at least one live or stillborn calf in Oman by July 1986. The matrilines show that the females' contributions were very unequal. For each female there were qualitative correlations of 'poor quality', such as poor condition either all the time or during late pregnancy, or a highly nervous temperament in an otherwise good breeding female. In one case, a female's poor condition was associated with faecal nitrogen levels 25% higher than her herd's average when on common grazing or supplementary feed. The two males which died in the wild were both behaviourally uncompetitive, and one exhibited sub-maxillary oedema after drinking, which suggested some circulatory inadequacy.

During the same period, 29 live and three still births were recorded. Of the former, five calves died before the age of 30 days, with another two dying at 1.7 and 29 months. This mortality is almost exactly that of free-range ungulates at Whipsnade Park (Kirkwood *et al.*, 1987). The causes of death in the Oman-born Oryx differed from those of the adults and included separation and loss after birth, one case of infanticide during a change of dominant herd male, two unviable calves, one case of massed attack by ravens, and one progressive central-nervous-system disorder in the oldest fatality.

Although no pattern of disease is detectable in these deaths and the overall rate is reassuringly low, mortality within 30 days of birth is a sensitive indicator of inbreeding-related effects (Templeton and Read, 1984). As the pedigree of each Oryx in Oman can still be traced back to the World Herd Founders, an inbreeding coefficient can be calculated for each. Whereas the average coefficient of the founders was 0.028, that of the Oman-born Oryx had more than doubled to 0.065, although 16% of this increase was due to one animal which was conceived in the USA from parents who were themselves half-sibs.

Although the sample size is still small, 30-day survival seems to decline sharply at coefficients above 0.075, which is well below the level of 0.125, equivalent to first-cousin crosses, which zoo breeding programmes use as a maximum inbreeding coefficient. The inbreeding coefficient is determined by the degree of relatedness of the parents who may not themselves be inbred. Figure 4.2 shows the 30-day survival of 30 out of 32 calves born in Oman sired by three males, against the average relatedness of each male to the females by which he bred. The implications for the re-introduction are clear: namely, that breeding males should be as genetically different from the females as possible.

Figure 4.2: Average inbreeding level of each male's calves and 30 day survival

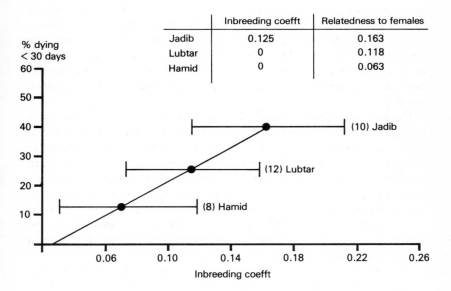

	Inbreeding coefft	Relatedness to females
Jadib	0.125	0.163
Lubtar	0	0.118
Hamid	0	0.063

An Assessment of Re-introduction Methods

In view of the management strategies described above, how successful have they been to date?

1. Herd Cohesion

Oryx deliberately separated from their herd either to isolate for a few days before calving, during which the female might move up to 60 kilometres from the herd, or during the first month after calving. Individuals or small splinter groups would occasionally leave to revisit previous ranges and single animals might walk to the release area to drink before returning to their herd. Accidental separations usually occurred at night when the separated animal(s) failed to detect the herd moving off. The behaviour of the Oryx concerned indicates whether the separation was deliberate or not. Combining both types, for Herd 1 from release to the end of 1985 (one month less than four years), separations started on less than 2.4% of all days, with the result that all members of the herd were together on all except 21% of days. This shows that herd cohesion was a very powerful force, resulting in efficient monitoring of herd and individual locations.

The cohesive herd structure was confirmed by the relationships between the two herds during the first two years that both lived in the desert. The two met for the first time at Yalooni when Herd 1 returned there after two months away and Herd 2 had been released from the enclosure two months previously. The herds contained 13 and 11 Oryx respectively. Over the next six weeks, there were many exchanges, either of single Oryx or of small groups, at the end of which only four animals were not in their original herds. Only two of these changes proved permanent, and both were males. This suggests that females are less likely to leave their original herds. Moreover, three out of four Oryx which changed herds found in their new herd another Oryx of the same sex and closer in age than in their previous herd.

When both herds lived around the release area during a dry period in 1984 and through 1985, the combined area of their two ranges was 300 km^2, of which only 24 km^2 were common to both. The herds never met during this period. Each dominant male squat-defaecated to demarcate his territory, but a low level of exchanges or visits between herds indicated that each herd was aware of the approximate location of the other.

In early 1986, sub-groups began to be recorded in both herds. These were of variable composition, lasted only a few days, and the sub-groups remained in the herd's current range without attempting to locate the others. When, in June 1986, heavy rain 50 kilometres south of Yalooni drew all the Oryx there, they moved in several small groups rather than in two discrete herds. Gradually, groups with Oryx from both original herds were increasingly recorded. This suggested that a fundamental change had occurred in the Oryx's ability to use their environment and showed their greater confidence in moving around independently and learning to locate one another, of which some impressive examples have been recorded. Oryx have also learnt that small groups can live on small areas of grazing which would either not support a larger herd at all, or support it only for a short period. This pattern of movement and dispersion seems far more the ancestral type, in which case early management of Oryx in Oman may have over-emphasised herd cohesion and promoted inter-herd intolerance. This approach, however, undoubtedly reduced the incidence of potentially fatal separations and loss, and reduced the chance of relatively desert-naïve Oryx mixing with and being led away by more experienced and hardy animals. The behaviour of the present smaller groups confirms the earlier thought that herds of more than 15 Oryx seemed fissile.

2. *Release-area Fidelity*

The pattern of sequential range use (Figure 4.1) shows how Herd 1 left the release area, and spent 22 months in a large total area before returning to Yalooni after a long rainless period. Monitoring the environmental conditions which led to this return showed that it was probably unavoidable for the Oryx. Their subsequent behaviour, and that of Herd 2 (for which the range of ecological conditions experienced was more limited), showed that Oryx would take advantage of the food and water supplied near Yalooni only if conditions were below maintenance standard in their total known range. If the air temperature dropped seasonally, the herd might return to a previous range to see if a water-free existence was possible and, of course, after rain the herd would move at once. This behaviour has two important management implications:

(a) Knowledge of the release area and its facilities of feed and water has resulted in no weaned Oryx being lost, to starve or die of thirst in the desert.

(b) The hospitality of the release area is clearly not preferred to living off the land naturally, and so is not abused when conditions allow independent existence. The corollary of this is that, if Oryx do return to the release area, there is no merit in withholding feed and/or water. This also shows that for re-introduction, in general, into unpredictable environments, the attainment of true independence by released animals may not be a continuous and unpunctuated process.

3. Security

Oryx have now lived free again in the desert for over five years, during which time there has been no single incident involving the local bedu and the Oryx. In general, potential disputes over competition for limited good grazing between Oryx and people and livestock are resolved through discussion, or result in the Oryx moving off. The Oryx themselves are not a perceived threat to any human activity and the re-introduction project is welcomed for its economic benefits and the services it provides. This fully justifies its expectations as a means of creating employment that should be appropriate to a remote desert area (Daly, this volume, page 16). In addition, the Harasis people are now aware of their pivotal role in making possible the Oryx's return, and are proud that their lands are the sole site of a unique living resource. The increasing participation of all Harasis (see below) in monitoring the Oryx population testifies to the acceptability of the re-introduction and the low likelihood of any local attempt to harm the Oryx.

The Future and Conclusions

The re-introduction efforts in Oman show that Oryx, the progeny of several generations of captive breeding, can be re-introduced into their native habitat to develop an independent existence with a highly developed ability to exploit their environment. Soon, calves will be born whose paternity can be deduced only from association at the relevant time. Thus, the precision of monitoring data will decrease as the population and the area used by the Oryx both increase. At a certain stage, depending on rainfall patterns and the experience of individual Oryx while growing up, some animals will have never visited Yalooni. If such Oryx are more likely to die of starvation or thirst, then probably the most important natural mortality factors will have started to operate.

It is evident from the written results of 'Operation Oryx' (Grimwood, 1962) and the opinions of the Harasis that the re-introduced Oryx behave in many ways exactly as did the ancestral population. It is, however, unlikely that the re-introduced population can ever be an exact mimic of its predecessor, for several reasons:

1. Accidents of discovery: at least some of the former Oryx used a

few very specific water sources, such as the brackish coastal creeks. It is highly unlikely that any of the re-introduced Oryx would locate these, largely because of the extent of settlement on the coastal plain. The water seepages along the Huqf escarpment may fall into the same category.

2. Although the present Oryx have discovered none, there has been considerable water development on the Jiddat-al-Harasis. Once any source other than Yalooni is known and used, the Oryx's perception and pattern of use of the Jidda' and its resources may change radically.

3. The aboriginal Oryx had no long-term fidelity to one area, such as Yalooni. Although this fidelity has many advantages, it may continue to influence the Oryx population for many generations.

4. Although the period between extinction and re-introduction was only ten years, it spanned great changes in the Harasis way of life which switched from subsistence pastoralism to a motorised, semi-nomadic form of livestock-raising. This was accompanied by profound economic and social changes, with the simple consequence that the bedu's priorities and pattern of land use have changed radically. Not all these changes are adverse to re-establishing Oryx, but they will ensure that the modern Oryx can never exploit their environment exactly as their predecessors did. Nonetheless, if the efforts of the re-introduction project since 1980 in the field can be sustained, Oman should be able to continue to claim a re-established population of the Arabian Oryx. In doing so, it will have played a pioneering role in the growing use of re-introductions as a conservation technique and will have re-created a living, renewable resource of which its government and people are rightly proud.

References

Daly, R.H. (1985) 'And what' said the Sultan, 'shall we do about the oryx?' *Species Survival Commission Newsletter* 5: 25–7.

Grimwood, I.R. (1962) Operation Oryx. *Oryx VI* No. 6: 308–34.

Henderson, D.S. (1974) Were they the last Arabian Oryx? *Oryx 12*: 347–50.

Jungius, H. (1985) The Arabian Oryx: Its distribution and former habitat in Oman and its re-introduction. *J. Oman Studies 8*: 49–64.

Kirkwood, J.K., Gaskin, C.D., and Markham, J. (1987) Perinatal mortality and season of birth in captive wild ungulates. *Veterinary Record 120*: 386–90.

Templeton, A.R., and Read, B. (1984) Factors eliminating inbreeding depression in a captive herd of Speke's gazelle (*Gazella spekei*). *Zoo Biology 3*: 177–99.

5. Re-introduction of the Arabian Oryx into Jordan

Maher Z. Abu Jafar and Copelia Hays-Shahin

History

The Arabian Oryx *Oryx leucoryx* was originally distributed through-out the desert regions of the Arabian Peninsula, extending north to the Syrian Desert. It has been hunted by man since ancient times for its meat, light-coloured coat and long horns, but with the development of organised hunting using traps the Oryx declined drastically. By the 1930s, the Arabian Oryx was extinct in Jordan (Clarke, 1977).

Re-introduction Programme

The Shaumari Wildlife Reserve, founded in 1975 by the Royal Society for the Conservation of Nature (RSCN), was established for the re-introduction of indigenous wildlife. The reserve is located in the eastern semi-arid region of Jordan (Figure 5.1), within the northern limit of the Arabian Oryx's distribution. Its 22 km^2 are totally fenced, and the prevention of grazing by domestic stock has allowed the indigenous vegetation cover to regenerate completely. The area is characterised by flat or undulating plains of limestone hammada, intersected by wadis which are seasonal water courses and depressions which display a diverse vegetation of shrubs, herbs and grasses. The alluvial soil which collects in the floor of the wadis provides for abundant growth of grasses.

A breeding unit and isolation pens were constructed at Shau-mari, and in 1978 eight Oryx—four males and four females—were sent from the World Herd. An additional three animals were sent from Qatar. The first phase of the re-introduction project was maximum production of offspring in order to produce a viable group of Arabian Oryx. The initial herd of 11 animals adapted quickly and bred successfully, and by 1983 the herd had increased to 31 individuals (15 males and 16 females). Under the patronage of HM King Hussein of Jordan and HRH The Duke of Edinburgh, the herd was released in October 1983 into the 22-km² tract of the Wildlife Reserve.

Figure 5.1: Jordan and the Shaumari Reserve

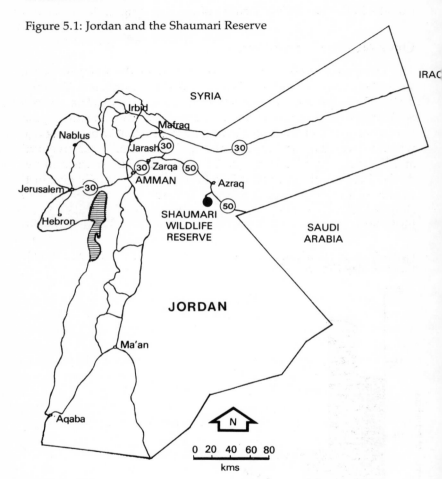

Management

The Arabian Oryx now breed under fully natural conditions and human interference is kept to a minimum, occurring only in the case of disease or when a calf is born. Calves are captured within two days of birth, sexed and ear-notched with an appropriate breeding number, which allows for identification at a distance. Daily patrols on horseback are made by the two rangers, who keep a record of their observations. Since no free water is available inside the reserve, 120 litres of water are supplied daily in drinking troughs in the immediate vicinity of the breeding unit.

Oryx Numbers and Dynamics

The Oryx have been increasing steadily over the 4½-year period since their release, and as of May 1987 they numbered 70 individuals. This represents a population increase of 126%. The sex ratio is 32 males to 38 females. Age distribution of the current population is shown in Figure 5.2: 32 Oryx (46%) are below breeding age, which is two years on average, although one female did give birth at 1.8 years; the remaining 38 (54%) are sexually mature individuals. The gestation period is 240 days and Oryx usually give birth to only one calf (although a female did miscarry twins on one occasion). From June 1979 to May 1987, there has been a total of 66 live births from 20 females, 14 of whom were themselves born at Shaumari.

Figure 5.2: Age distribution of the Arabian Oryx herd at Shaumari Wildlife Reserve, May 1987 (n = 70)

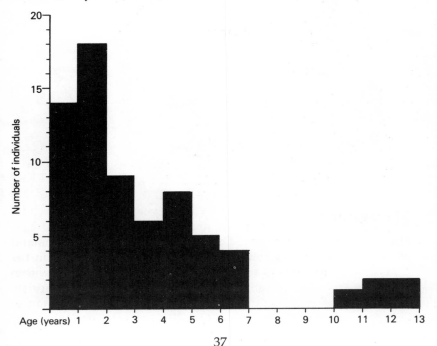

37

It appears that as the Oryx adapt to the surrounding natural conditions they become seasonal breeders. At Shaumari, the majority of births occur between October and May (Figure 5.3), and a similar trend of breeding seasonality is apparent in Oman (Jackson, 1986). Although in Oman the seasonality of births is attributed to a limited water supply in summer, at Shaumari the herd is supplied daily with fresh drinking water. Therefore, water does not appear to be the limiting factor.

Figure 5.3: Monthly distribution of Arabian Oryx births at Shaumari Reserve, Jordan, from 1979 to 1986

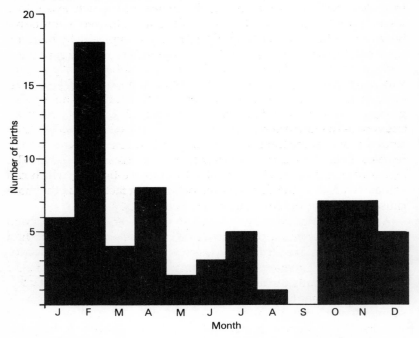

The Oryx feed mainly on grasses, and Eykenduyn (1985), while conducting a pilot study at Shaumari, noted that areas of the Reserve most favoured by the Oryx were where grasses were most abundant. A total of 21 grass species has been recorded by Clarke (1977) and Eykenduyn assumed that the Oryx feed on most, if not all, species present. He also noted that, when the availability of grasses decreased, the Oryx shifted to eating more shrubs such as Sidlitzia, Capparis, Tamarisk and Citrullus.

38

Since the herd's release, there have been a total of 13 deaths. The major cause of adult mortality is fighting among the males. Of the six adults that died, four were males whose deaths were due to fights. One of the adult females died while giving birth and another one was bitten by a poisonous snake. The other seven deaths were of young Oryx, under four months old; the causes of death were various. Overall mortality rate is relatively low at 15%.

Social Organisation and Herd Size

This species exhibits a strong social hierarchy that is very apparent in a clear ranking order among the males and which exists to a lesser extent among the females. All males showed submissive behaviour when approaching the alpha-male, typically by bending their head towards the ground yet maintaining the horns pointed backwards while flicking the ears and the tail. Submissive behaviour was also shown throughout the hierarchy by subordinates to higher-ranking males who were usually observed in one of the smaller groups. The lowest-ranking males, considered 'outcasts', received frequent horn blows from all the other adults, including females. They tended to stay at the fringe of the group and were submissive even to females. Every two or three years there is a change in leadership. The alpha-male and his rival are involved in intense fighting which can sometimes lead to the death of one of them. In fact, this is the main cause of mortality among adult males (see above).

A clear ranking order does not exist among females, although in general the older and more experienced females ranked higher than the younger females. Submissive behaviour to high-ranking males was exhibited by females on some occasions, but usually one of the older females leads the herd and the alpha-male takes up the rear.

Highly pregnant females or those that had just given birth were seen only with the alpha-male; no other males were allowed in the vicinity. The pregnant female gives birth in solitude, leaving the herd four to 24 hours before delivering. The alpha-male frequently visits the female and calf in the period that they are away from the main group, which may range from two to three months.

The Arabian Oryx at Shaumari are divided into two main groups. One is located to the north, with 45 individuals, and the other is in the southeast of the Reserve, with 25 animals. The main group will divide into temporary smaller groups ranging from one to 15 individuals.

Daily Activity

The Oryx start to graze shortly after sunrise and continue until about 9.00 a.m., when they head towards the drinking area. Here they stay for between 1½ and two hours. After resting, they head back to graze. At dusk they locate an adequate area for the night, and it is usually among high vegetation that they lie down.

Carrying Capacity

The re-introduction of the Arabian Oryx to its natural habitat has been a real success at Shaumari Wildlife Reserve; but we must now face the question of carrying capacity. Two limiting factors are involved: food and space. With regard to food availability, Clarke (1977) had suggested a carrying capacity of 77 individuals. In terms of space, Eykenduyn (1986) assumed that the carrying capacity would not exceed 70 individuals. Based on initial results from a preliminary study conducted by two professors from the University of Jordan, it has been shown that the impact of the Arabian Oryx currently grazing on the vegetation at Shaumari is minimal. These two researchers estimate that the vegetation at Shaumari can support up to *300* individuals. Presently there are no signs of over-grazing, but this has been a very wet year and abundant plant growth should be available. In terms of space, 'social stress' is not evident among the herd. To avoid symptoms of over-crowding, however, expansion of the reserve to 320 km^2 is currently in progress under the guidance of the Royal Society for the Conservation of Nature.

References

Clarke, J.E. (1977) Shaumari Wildlife Reserve Plan. Unpub. MS for Royal Society for the Conservation of Nature, Amman, Jordan.

Eykenduyn, F.G. (1985) *The Oryx in Jordan.* Report for Royal Society for the Conservation of Nature, Amman, Jordan.

Eykenduyn, F.G. (1986) *A proposal for future research on the Arabian Oryx in Shaumari.* Report for Royal Society for the Conservation of Nature, Amman, Jordan.

Jackson, P. (1986) Back on the wild side—the Oryx in Oman. *WWF Monthly Report*, October: 255–9.

6. The Arabian Oryx Programme in Saudi Arabia

Abdulaziz H. Abu-Zinada, Kushal Habibi and Roland Seitre

Introduction

The Arabian Oryx *Oryx leucoryx* has captivated the hearts and minds of the people of the Arabian Peninsula from time immemorial. Admired as a symbol of strength and endurance, the Oryx has been eulogised by Arab poets, who described it as a twinkling light glittering in the sky and a blade shining in the darkness of the night (Ghandour, 1987). On a practical level, the Oryx has played a major traditional role in the life of the Arab people. Its flesh was considered an invigorating delicacy (Philby, 1933). Bedouins, according to Thomas (1932), used the facial skin of the Oryx as a rifle-butt cover and gave the solid contents of its stomach to their camels. Its skin was used for leather, its blood for snake bites and its soup for joint pains. The nomadic tribes which shared the Oryx's traditional habitats believed that its meat gave man strength, potency and vigour (Stewart, 1963). But, despite the poetic euphoria and the material benefits, the Oryx has had to struggle to survive in the present century. Today, the species is a symbol of the fragility of arid ecosystems, which, when damaged, take decades to recover their original form.

Once widespread throughout the Arabian Peninsula and ranging up to the Euphrates (Stewart, 1963), the Arabian Oryx became rare towards the beginning of this century. With an increase in human activity and the availability of modern firearms, most of the Oryx inside the Arabian Pensinsula were eliminated. By the 1930s, the Arabian Oryx was distributed in two separate detachments. One was the northern Nafud population and the other was in the south, concentrated in and around the vast expanses of the Rub-al-Khali Desert (Carruthers, 1935).

In the north, the Oryx was hunted to extinction in the 1950s; the

41

last Oryx tracks were seen in the Nafud in 1954 (Dolan, 1973). In the south, hunting pressure had increased during the 1960s to the extent that there seemed little hope for the animals' survival in the wild, as Talbot (1960) had predicted. Motorised transportation, which became popular a quarter of a century ago, accelerated the total elimination of the species from the wild (Dolan, 1976). By 1972, the last wild Arabian Oryx was believed to have been killed or captured (Henderson, 1974). Recent unconfirmed reports, however, seem to place the last observations of the Oryx in the wild at eight to nine years ago. A pair was reportedly seen during 1978 and a single animal was spotted in 1979 on the northern edge of the Rub-al-Khali. It is possible that, true to the species' reputation for endurance, one or two Oryx may have survived in its southern range up to a decade ago, despite international pressure aimed at hunting or capturing the animals alive.

The Breeding Programme

Unfortunately, there seems to be very little information on the history of the species in captivity in the Kingdom of Saudi Arabia except that animals occurred in Riyadh Zoo and in some private collections. Four of the original World Herd, two males and two females, came from the collection of HM King Saud bin Abdul Aziz, so, from the onset of 'Operation Oryx', the Kingdom has been involved in the welfare and revitalisation of the Arabian Oryx. Subsequently, HM the late King Khalid initiated a breeding programme by concentrating some animals from the Kingdom on his farm at Thumamah about 80 kilometres north of Riyadh. Animals from collections in neighbouring countries and the World Herd were added to the Saudi stock, but unfortunately, owing to crowded conditions in the enclosure, calf mortality was high and a number of animals succumbed to various diseases (Habibi, 1986). Thus, the rate of increase was less than expected.

In early 1986, HRH Prince Saud al Faisal took the initiative to establish the National Commission for Wildlife Conservation and Development (NCWCD) on behalf of HM King Fahd bin Abdul Aziz. One of the Commission's main duties is to re-establish wild and self-sustaining populations of endemic species, including the Arabian Oryx. As part of a scientifically based captive-breeding programme, two National Wildlife Research Centres have been established near Taif and Thumamah.

Breeding Facilities

The idea of the breeding programme at the National Wildlife Research Centre in Taif is to preserve the animals in an enclosure which depicts natural conditions as much as possible. For each breeding herd, 15 to 25 hectares of natural vegetation have been selected. These pens allow free movement and the animals are able to select palatable vegetation from a wide range of plants occurring in the Centre. Movements and cover are facilitated and the young are able to hide, thus preserving their natural behaviour. Supplementary food is provided in an 8 × 15 metre capture facility.

Each pen, which is considered an animal-breeding unit, consists of one male and five or six females plus their calves. Young males are removed from the breeding unit before the onset of aggressive behaviour when they are about six months old. Bachelor males are kept in separate pens. Owing to the small size of the herd, young females are kept with the breeding unit. With the expansion of the breeding units, young females will be placed with an adult female to form a breeding group of their own with one adult male.

Health

At Taif, all animals suspected of tuberculosis are kept apart, as are tuberculin test-positive animals. Out of four calves born to infected mothers, all were found to be negative to TB tests. These animals have been released into a breeding enclosure. So far, five animals are undergoing treatment. Two of these have completed treatment, and currently both are negative to the test.

To minimise wounds, rubber hoses are glued to the tips of horns. This is because even minor wounds can induce septicaemic pasteurellosis. This disease is difficult to cure since infected animals show few symptoms of the disease until lesions are extensive.

Out of the 17 calves born at the Centre, one abortion occurred after transportation. One TB-positive female lost her calf four days prior to her death and one fully grown foetus was stillborn. Two casualties have occurred among the young born at Taif, one dying from pneumonia and the other from caecal torsion.

Anticipated Herd Size

It is envisaged that the size of the herd will be increased to about 80 animals, which may take up to five years. By then, release sites will have been established. Two groups of about 20 animals, composed of a breeding nucleus together with calves, will be available for re-introduction into the wild in the release sites.

Plans are also underway to construct captive-breeding facilities at Thumamah, where 14 animals from the original herd are still maintained. The female-to-male ratio at Thumamah is skewed towards the males, with only three breeding females there at present. With the completion of breeding facilities towards the end of summer, however, it is expected that three or four additional females will be added to the Thumamah Centre in order to increase the breeding pool.

Re-introduction

Pronounced wanderers, the Oryx cover great distances in search of food and can go for many months without water. They derive water from dew and moisture contained in vegetation (Jungius, 1985). Thesiger (1947) and Stewart (1963) state that, at times of good grazing, the Oryx stay in sand dunes but move to wadi beds because of heat and lack of shade. Such seasonal migration patterns suggest that re-introduction sites for the Oryx should be large enough in size to cover an extensive array of habitats which will meet the food and cover requirements of the species during various seasons of the year.

On the basis of the known social behaviour and migration patterns of the Arabian Oryx, it will be necessary to choose a re-introduction site where the animals occurred prior to their exter-mination in Saudi Arabia. The Al-Arid, along the western edge of the Rub-al-Khali, is one such area which has good re-introduction potential. This site, and others, will be studied in detail before any decisions are made. Prior to any transplantation, range conditions in the release area have to be improved and the area protected from the onslaught of livestock exploitation. Once pasture conditions show adequate signs of improvement and the site is adequately protected, re-introduction of the animals can be contemplated. A public-awareness programme will be started to inform citizens of the biological and historic significance of the Arabian Oryx in our society in order to encourage their participation in the programme.

Taking into account the experience gained through the Oryx re-introduction programme in the Sultanate of Oman, the released animals will undergo an acclimatisation programme in an enclosure within the release area. Such an acclimatisation, which may take several years to complete, will allow the captive-reared animals to adapt to natural conditions. This will also facilitate the animals' becoming acquainted with the game wardens and help control their movements once the animals are released in the wild as the herd becomes familiar with the release site and discovers new feeding locations.

Conclusions

The Arabian Oryx has been a vital component in the life and culture of the people of Saudi Arabia. Its ruthless destruction reminds us of a missing element in our native fauna. The re-introduction of Oryx into the wild will not only be of great aesthetic and biological value, but will also enable us to contribute to international conservation efforts in the peninsula.

In parallel with the Arabian Oryx rehabilitation programme, plans are underway to start a breeding programme of rare and endangered species of endemic gazelles *Gazella* spp. Research on their behaviour, nutrition and pathology will be started at both the Thumamah and the Taif Research Centres. Apart from the captive-breeding programme, the Commission is also undertaking ecological studies of the Kingdom's wildlife to assess its status and distribution. These studies will help in formulating a sound strategy for a national system plan of protected areas in the country.

References

Carruthers, D. (1935) *Arabian Adventure to the Great Nafud in Quest of the Oryx*. Witherby, London.

Dolan, J.M. (1973) The return of the Unicorn. *Zoonooz 46*: 6–10.

Dolan, J.M. (1976) The Arabian Oryx: Its destruction, captive history and propagation. *Inter. Zoo Ybk 16*: 230–9.

Ghandour, A.M. (1987) *The Oryx: From Captivity to Reintroduction*. NCWCD Pub. No. 1, Riyadh.

Habibi, K. (1986) Arabian ungulates—their status and future protection. *Oryx 20*: 100–3.

Henderson, D.S. (1974) Were they the last Arabian Oryx? *Oryx 12*: 347–50.

Jungius, H. (1985) The Arabian Oryx: Its distribution and former habitat in Oman and its reintroduction. *J. Oman Studies 8*: 49–64.

Philby H. St J.B. (1933) *The Empty Quarter, being a description of the great south desert of Arabia known as Rub-al-Khali*. London.

Stewart, D.R.M. (1963) The Arabian oryx (*Oryx Leucoryx* Pallas). *E. African Wildlife Journal 1*: 103–17.

Talbot, L.M. (1960) *A Look at Threatened Species*. Fauna Preservation Society, London.

Thesiger, W. (1947) A new journey in southern Arabia. *Geographical Journal 8*.

Thomas, B. (1932) *Arabia felix: Across the empty quarter of Arabia.*

7. The Arabian Oryx in Captivity with Particular Reference to the Herds in Arabia

David M. Jones

Early History

The Arabian Oryx *Oryx leucoryx* was first described in some detail by the Russian naturalist Pallas in 1777, although there are almost certainly references to the species in the Bible (Deuteronomy 33:17), where it was referred to as the unicorn: 'His glory is like the firstling of his bullock and his horns are like the horns of unicorns.' Pennant, in his history of quadrupeds (1781), describes the animal from drawings of captive animals belonging to the Shah of Persia, made in 1712. At that time, however, there was considerable confusion over the identification of the Arabian and the Scimitar-horned Oryx (*Oryx dammah*), the latter often being referred to in older literature as the Leucoryx.

Dolan, from whose comprehensive review (1976) much of this early history of the species is taken, records a number of animals as having arrived in European collections during the last century. One animal of unknown sex arrived in Amsterdam in 1848 and one in London in 1956, these to be followed by others given mainly as gifts by military personnel working in Arabia or by Arab leaders. The first London animal was originally thought to have been an immature Gemsbok (*Oryx gazella gazella*), but J.E. Gray of the Natural History Museum recognised the much paler animal as a new species and proposed the name *Oryx beatrix*.

Distribution

Originally, the animal occurred throughout much of the Arabian Peninsula from the Sinai north to Mesopotamia, and it was probably still fairly common throughout its range until the 1850s. By the turn of the century, very few Oryx survived in the northern part of its range, and, with the Turkish occupation of much of

Arabia during the early years of the First World War, this population was rapidly eliminated.

In 1935, Carruthers described two surviving populations over 1,100 kilometres apart; one was in the northern Nafud (on the borders of present-day Jordan and Saudi) and the other in the southern wilderness of the Rub-al-Khali (along the Oman-Saudi border). The developing oil industry brought with it four-wheel-drive vehicles, which, with modern firearms, contributed more than anything else to the extermination of the Oryx. The Nafud population probably died out in the 1950s, and by the time of the inception of plans for 'Operation Oryx' the Rub-al-Khali population was down to fewer than 200 animals.

Breeding in Captivity

The World Herd was founded in 1962: with two males and a female from the 'Operation Oryx' expedition; a female each from The Zoological Society of London and HH Sheikh Jaber Abdullah al Sabah, the ruler of Kuwait (1963); and two pairs from HM King Saud of Saudi Arabia (1964). Records of prior breeding in captivity between 1848 and 1963 are very scanty, although there were births at Dresden, Cairo, Washington, the Bronx (New York) and Philadelphia Zoos. Hybridisation between oryx species also occurred, and it has been a problem to this day, particularly in some of the Middle Eastern herds. In 1975, Dolan, the international studbook-keeper, recorded 64 animals in the USA (33:31) housed in three institutions—Phoenix, San Diego and Los Angeles. He believed then that there were about 35 animals in Arabia, but the author's investigation suggests that this was probably a considerable under-estimate. It is likely that there were at least this number in Qatar alone at that time, and there were certainly other small herds in both Abu Dhabi and Saudi, originating from different wild-caught sources. Today, there are about 420 animals in 15 groups in Arabia (Table 7.1).

There are also about 370 animals outside Arabia in at least 25 groups. In the United States, there are approximately 260 in 16 collections, in Europe 50 in seven collections, and ten in a single herd at Rabat Zoo in Morocco; in addition, there are about 40 animals in Israel and a few in the Far East. Those in the USA came either from the World Herd, established at Phoenix (Turkowski and Mohney, 1972) and later extended with animals sent from

Table 7.1: Approximate current numbers of Arabian Oryx in Arabian countries (numbers of known herds in brackets)

Qatar	100 (2)	Bahrain	45 (1)
Abu Dhabi	80 (3)	Oman	40 (2)
Jordan	75 (1)	Dubai	15 (1)
Saudi Arabia	55 (3)	Others	10 (2)

Total = 420

there to San Diego, or from Los Angeles, who purchased a male and two females (a pair and their calf) from the Dutch dealer Franz Van Den Brink in 1966. These animals came from the Riyadh Zoo, and it is not known whether the World Herd animals which came from Saudi and those which went to Los Angeles were related. All the European stock and those in Rabat come from the San Diego group of the World Herd.

Herds in the USA and Europe

The Arabian Oryx in the USA have done very well. The original three herds, particularly the one at San Diego, have seeded new Oryx groups elsewhere in the United States, in Europe and in Saudi, and have supplied animals for the re-introduction programmes in Oman and Jordan. There is no doubt that, under good management, this is a highly prolific species which presents few problems for captive management.

The situation in Europe has been less satisfactory, owing largely to a high preponderance of male births and to the deaths of the females sent to Rotterdam and their female progeny sent to London. Although these females bred, the majority of the calves born were male. East Berlin and Zurich also had predominantly male births at first. As a result, there are now twice as many males as females in Europe and this has clearly reduced the efficiency of the breeding programme. However, more females have been provided from the United States, and the herd at Hannover, which did not breed originally, has now produced a number of calves. A new group will shortly be established at Antwerp. There is therefore no reason now for the species not to do as well in Europe as in the United States. Currently, the breeding groups are in East Berlin, Zurich and Hannover, with a new young group in London and all-male groups in Rotterdam, Whipsnade and Marwell.

The international studbook and the regional studbook for the USA are based at San Diego, and the regional studbook for Europe and Morocco is based at London.

The Situation in Arabia

As a result of travelling extensively through many Arabian countries in recent years, the author has been able to collect more accurate data on the situation with regard to the Arabian Oryx in captivity there than has been available in the past. Unfortunately, it is still difficult to obtain accurate data from the managers of some of the herds there, largely because the majority of animals are effectively in private hands, usually those of the ruling families. There is, as yet, no co-operative breeding programme in the Arabian area and, with a few exceptions, the origins of the animals and their individual identifications are unknown.

In Qatar, there are approximately 100 animals at the Ministry of Agriculture's specifically established farm at Shahaniyah in the centre of the country. This herd originated from a number of capture expeditions south of the Rub-al-Khali in Saudi and western Oman. These were mounted by the members of the Qatari ruling family, principally a previous Minister of Agriculture, Sheikh Jassim, in the late 1950s and early 1960s. Unfortunately, no-one in Qatar that the author has questioned knows exactly where these expeditions took place, but it is probable that the capture of the live animals was initially a by-product of hunting trips when substantial numbers of these animals were also killed. Later, the expeditions concentrated on bringing back live animals. The Qataris may have felt that they were contributing to the survival of the species by catching animals to establish a breeding herd, but they also played a significant role in the demise of the last remaining wild populations. Whether they could have been saved from other hunters if protection had been applied at this time is debatable.

Originally, the herd was built up at Sheikh Jassim's private farm at Al Sulaimi in Qatar, in a large walled enclosure. However, owing to severe over-crowding and the proximity of large numbers of domestic animals, notably goats, the group was continually afflicted by a succession of disease outbreaks, and numbers grew only slowly. In 1979, an impending State visit by HM Queen Elizabeth and HRH The Duke of Edinburgh led to the Qataris building a special farm for the animals at Shahaniyah so that they could be viewed more easily. As a result, the herd at Sulaimi was divided and 17 animals were sent to start the new facility. A further five animals were added from a private collection at Al Wokra, south of Doha. Those at Shahaniyah have done reasonably well; but the animals at the original farm have declined in numbers and, following an outbreak of what was probably rinderpest in 1984, combined with the social effects of the predominance of adult males in the herd who were continually fighting, the group has all but died out. Animals from the Shahaniyah group have now been sent to Kuwait, Iraq, Saudi and Bahrain, and Shahaniyah contributed four of the founder animals to the very successful herd at Shaumari in Jordan.

The animals at Shahanyah have much more space than they had at Sulaimi and they are now kept in four groups. Their management is, however, still relatively unscientific in comparison with that of the other principal groups of the species. Many of the animals are overweight, there are too many adult males kept with the breeding females, veterinary attention could be improved, and the whole programme for their care needs organising in the light of current knowledge of the species. It is probable that calf output could also be increased. Potentially, this is the most important herd in the Middle East and it is hoped that the Ministry of Agriculture and the Qatari Royal Family can be persuaded that the management of these Oryx must be more professional if they are to flourish.

The next largest group is that at Shaumari in Jordan, which now numbers over 70 animals, the majority of which have been released into the wildlife reserve there. These animals, which are managed by the Royal Society for the Conservation of Nature, come from American and Qatari stock. The breeding programme has been particularly successful, and other re-introductions are planned in Jordan using the progeny.

There are three known groups in Abu Dhabi, the largest of which is based at the Al Ain Zoo and now numbers about 60 animals. These are believed to have originated from a male and two females caught in Saudi Arabia and they are unrelated to any other groups in the Middle East. Two other smaller groups, totalling some 20 animals, are in the private collections of the ruler's family and these animals are believed to originate from another quite separate line of wild-caught individuals. Next door to Abu Dhabi, Sheikh Mohammed in the Emirate of Dubai has a small group, most of which, if not all, probably came from American stock. In Oman, all the animals for the re-introduction project except two come from American stock; the other individuals are from Jordan and Bahrain. Further imports from the USA and Jordan are expected shortly, but currently there are approximately 35 animals in the release area and a small group at the Sultan's private breeding station in Muscat. Despite some minor nutritional and toxicological problems with the main herds, the groups are expanding under careful management and there is now an urgent need to provide more animals for release as soon as they can be made available.

In Saudi Arabia, a group of Oryx has been maintained on the Royal farm at Thumamah, northwest of Riyadh, for ten years, but its origins are not clear. It is known that some 18 animals were sent to Saudi Arabia in the mid-1970s from the United States and that most of these probably went to Thumamah, where they would have been joined by the residue of a herd which came from a Royal collection in the city of Riyadh and perhaps animals from the old Riyadh Zoo. These could well have been the same groups which provided animals for the original World Herd and for Los Angeles. The quality of the management of these various groups has varied over the years, probably involving a great deal of care in the early 1960s but having been less efficient in the 1970s and early 1980s. Although quite a number of Oryx no doubt died during this latter period, there were approximately 70 animals on the farm when the newly formed National Commission for Wildlife Conservation and Development took over their management in early 1986. The majority of these were caught up for air shipment to the new research station at Taif. In the process of this exercise, however, it was discovered that the animals were suffering from an endemic problem with bovine tuberculosis. The Oryx at Thumamah had been enclosed with large numbers of gazelles *Gazella* spp. and other ungulate species, and the evidence so far suggests that the infection probably originated from Fallow Deer *Cervus dama* imported some years earlier from Spain. It is likely that the stress of capture and movement, together with their relocation in new groups at a new site, created the background conditions for the disease to become clinically manifest in the Oryx, although it may have been a cause of death previously, before routine post-mortem examinations were carried out. Detailed investigations on this problem have begun at Taif and at Thumamah, where a second wildlife research station is being established. If the TB-eradication programme goes well, some of the 50 surviving animals will form herds for the re-introduction schemes now planned over the next decade in Saudi Arabia. In the meantime, it is hoped that the schemes can progress with animals from some of the herds outside the Kingdom.

The only other large herd of Arabian Oryx in the Arabian Gulf area is that maintained at the Al Areen reserve in Bahrain. Two separate groups are kept here, one from the Qatar stock and the other originating from Saudi animals donated to Bahrain before the Saudi groups were merged with American stock. These are well-managed groups which are expanding steadily and where all the individuals are identifiable, a situation which is achieved elsewhere in the Gulf area only in Oman, and now in Saudi Arabia.

It is probable that there are also two small groups surviving in Kuwait and Iraq which originally came from the Qatar family lines but which have not yet done well. Jordan is understood to be donating a few animals to Iraq shortly to try to increase the reproductive potential of the Baghdad herd. As co-operation in the management of this important species in Arabia improves, it is to be hoped that a regional studbook can be established and that reports are made regularly to the international studbook-keeper.

Outside the Arab world in the Middle East, there is a group of about 40 animals maintained at Hai-bar in southern Israel, all of which originated from American stock. A re-introduction project is being planned for them shortly.

The General Situation in Arabia

Because the Arabian Oryx is such a rare animal, with great cultural and symbolic significance for the Arab nations, the two most important objectives of any internationally organised programme to save the species must be to provide sufficient individuals for well-planned re-introduction programmes and to use those in captivity for suitable exhibition and educational purposes. So far, efforts to provide the facilities for realistic re-introduction programmes have been limited to Oman and Jordan, with Saudi Arabia now making considerable progress as well. The great majority of the animals involved in these programmes, however, have come from American stock, most of which originated from the World Herd, so fulfilling the purpose of its establishment in

1962. Animals will continue to come from that source, but the time has now come for all the Arab countries holding this species also to co-operate fully in encouraging the rapid development of re-introduction programmes. After all, the herds were founded on animals captured in Saudi Arabia and Oman. The Oryx is a keynote species for conservation in Arabia, and the publicity and educational value which result from these programmes will encourage the other forms of environmental care and conservation which are so badly needed there at present.

In contrast to the situation outside Arabia, all the principal family lines of captive Arabian Oryx are now represented in the Arabian herds. Two are in Abu Dhabi, one in Qatar, one in Bahrain and the other, the 'American line', is represented in Jordan, Oman and Saudi Arabia. There is, therefore, a considerable genetic pool from which to draw animals and it is most important that maximum use be made of it. For this reason, six males are to be imported from Bahrain (from both groups) into Europe to provide new blood for the herds there and for America, but more transfers are necessary. It is important that Oryx from Abu Dhabi in particular, as well as from Qatar, should be introduced as soon as possible into the groups currently being managed for re-introduction purposes and into the breeding herds in America and Europe.

It is essential to try to establish a regional studbook or at least a species register for the Arabian countries and to try to get some form of agreement between the managers of the various herds towards a common approach to conserving the species. As far as is practical, efforts need to be made to identify all the individual Oryx by ear-tagging and tattooing, and there needs to be considerable improvement in the management of some of the herds, notably that in Qatar. Experienced help and advice is available and should be sought. In this respect, the groups need to be made the responsibility of people with specific knowledge of managing captive wild ungulates, particularly antelopes, and who can utilise the latest technology in capture techniques; veterinary care, especially of skin and feet; disease prevention; population genetics; and nutrition, with special reference to energy and protein intake and trace-element metabolism. There is little doubt that with good management some of these herds could be much more productive than they are at present, and this has been quite clearly shown with the improvements that have taken place in the care of some of these groups in the last few years. There is, for example, great reluctance to handle the animals for marking and for routine veterinary checks and treatment, despite the fact that, in skilled hands, this is not a difficult species to anaesthetise. It is possible that a few animals may be lost under anaesthesia, but the overall results in terms of improved breeding performance and the survival of calves are always such that the growth in numbers and therefore the potential for providing animals for re-introduction projects increase considerably.

Having said all this, it is worth remembering that full-scale re-introduction programmes are probably going to be feasible only in Oman, Jordan and Saudi Arabia at the present time, with more limited programmes being possible in the Emirates, Kuwait and, perhaps in the future, Iraq. In the smaller Emirates and in Qatar and Bahrain, this species is always going to be held at best in a park situation. Nevertheless, the educational value of even limited programmes is considerable.

The Wider Horizon

It has been suggested recently that more animals should be coming back to Arabia more quickly from the American and European herds for re-introduction purposes. Another group is being sent from the United States in 1988 to add to those already involved in the Omani programme. What needs to be remembered, however, is that, although there are well over 300 animals outside the Arabian Peninsula, only about 90 of these are currently breeding females. The Arabian herds have twice the breeding potential. Given that the Gulf area is not altogether politically stable and that there is still some way to go before full co-operation develops between those holding these animals in the Gulf region, the re-introduction programmes are still going to be dependent to a considerable extent for some years to come on the breeding herds outside the area. It is therefore vital for the species as a whole that the breeding groups providing animals for re-introduction are maintained in the best possible physical and genetic health. Otherwise, the very basis of the programme for the conservation of this species could be undermined. It is probable that the re-introduction programme in Oman started somewhat earlier than it should have done. Carefully thought-out and expensive facilities were established at Yalooni with the hope that there would be a continuous stream of animals going through them 'en route' to full release. This has not been the case and, had the programme been started ten years later, the prospect of having such a continuous flow would have been much better. Nevertheless, this programme, in addition to drawing the attention of the world, has been an integral part of a very much wider-ranging conservation programme in Oman and as such has helped to focus attention on other environmental issues. In the future, it is likely that other large mammal re-introduction programmes will have to take more risks with the available animals. This is partly because governments and funding agencies will want to see results more quickly, but largely because most countries will not have the resources to invest in the sort of facilities that have been used in Oman and Jordan, and will be used in Saudi Arabia. The re-introduction programmes now being planned for such species as the Scimitar-horned Oryx *Oryx dammah*, the Addax *Addax nasomaculatus* and the Przewalski Horse *Equus przewalskii* can involve much larger numbers of animals in the initial phases with less preparation for release, because it is possible to provide hundreds rather than tens of these species thanks to the success of the captive-breeding programmes. Captive populations of these species are fast approaching the point where there will not be the room to hold them. The result is that a high proportion of the young animals now being born could be placed directly into re-introduction programmes. Risks are unavoidable and animals will be lost as they adapt to a new wild existence, so a programme to supply replacement animals quickly is very important.

Potentially, we are not far away from that situation with the Arabian Oryx, providing that all holders of these animals co-operate fully. By the end of 1988, there should be nearly 1,000 of them in captivity or in part of the existing release programmes. Under ideal conditions and with full international co-operation, the potential for calf production for these programmes could then be about 150 calves a year. If the programmes have to rely for the immediate future only on those institutions which have participated so far, then they will, however, be considerably restricted and much of the current interest and impetus may be lost.

References

Carruthers, D. (1935) *Arabian Adventure to the Great Nafud in Quest of the Oryx*. Witherby, London.

The Arabian Oryx in Captivity

Dolan, J.M. (1985) *The Arabian Oryx Studbook*. Zoo Soc. San Diego.

Dolan, J.M. (1976) The Arabian Oryx (*Oryx leucoryx*): its destruction, captive history and propagation. *Int. Zoo Ybk 16*: 230–9.

Fitter, R.S.R. (1982) Arabian Oryx returns to the wild. *Oryx 16*: 406–10.

Stanley Price, M.R. (1986) The reintroduction of the Arabian Oryx (*Oryx leucoryx*) into Oman. *Int. Zoo Ybk 24/25*: 179–88.

Turkowski, F.J., and Mohney, G.C. (1972) History, management and behaviour of the Phoenix Zoo Arabian Oryx herd 1964–71, *Spec. Bull. No. 2*, Arizona Zoo Soc.

8. The Genetic Status of the Arabian Oryx and the Design of Co-operative Management Programmes

Georgina M. Mace

Co-operative Breeding Programmes

'Operation Oryx', the establishment and early management of the World Herd of Arabian Oryx *Oryx leucoryx*, and the continuing re-introduction and release programmes, represent a fine example of what co-operation among different institutions and bodies can achieve for the benefit of rare species. This whole programme is also particularly important now as a model for other species, and, with more and more species facing extinction owing to rapid habitat loss, the need for such capture/captive-breeding/re-introduction programmes will continue to increase. In fact, as I will show in part of this paper, the Arabian Oryx programme has been remarkably successful and, compared with some other species which have been reduced to a handful of individuals, its genetic status is good. However, I also hope to demonstrate that continuing, long-term co-operative management of the species by all the different parties involved is essential if these initial efforts are not to have been in vain.

Before dealing in detail with a case study of the Arabian Oryx, it is relevant to consider the theory underlying the design of captive-breeding programmes. The design of any breeding programme must commence with a consideration of the ultimate aim of the project. In most domestic species, the aims are quite clear: they may be to increase milk production in dairy cattle or to increase egg production in poultry. Since we know that these are genetically based characteristics, a selective-breeding programme can be designed so that performance on these traits gradually improves over a number of generations. In the case of endangered species the aims are less clear-cut. Generally, we are presented with a situation in which we have only a small number of individuals in our care from which we wish to ensure a future for the species. In some cases, the prospects for re-introduction or release into the wild are remote. In others, re-introduction may be a realistic proposition within the relatively near future. Either way, it is unlikely that the environment in which the animal will be living several generations from now will be similar to the one in which it is presently found. Without a managed breeding programme there will be fairly rapid adaptation to the captive environment (Frankham *et al.*, 1986) and the individuals which are suited to captivity, either behaviourally or physiologically, will become the dominant breeding individuals. Individuals which had different traits, perhaps better suited to future environments, will be lost and with them the genetic variants they carried. Among rare species, the ultimate result of this can be that the species becomes increasingly restricted in the conditions under which it will thrive, and successful introductions into novel environments become impossible. Since we have no method of assessing the pressures in these future environments, nor the individuals that are best suited to them, the best approach is to maintain a maximum level of genetic diversity in the captive population. In this way, we have the best chance of preserving key genetic characteristics and we can allow the environment, by process of natural selection, to select the best-fitted individuals. As a result, therefore, a genetic aim for breeding plans for endangered species is the preservation of a maximum amount of genetic variation (Frankel and Soule, 1981).

There are three phases in any capture/captive-breeding/re-introduction programme at which genetic variation is lost. The first is at the stage when individuals are removed from the wild to form the founder stock for captive breeding. The more individuals that are used as founders, the higher the proportion of genetic variation retained. Often the number here is beyond the control of those managing the captive population, although, as is demonstrated below, the efforts of the early 'Operation Oryx' team to gather together ten instead of three or four individuals were well worthwhile. Secondly, during the period in captivity, genetic variation is lost with each generation, and, the smaller the population size, the smaller the proportion of the original variation that will be retained. Finally, at the time at which individuals are re-introduced into the wild, more will be lost if only a few individuals are re-introduced. Also, this stage is important as we can expect fairly high mortality rates as individuals with inappropriate genotypes and physiological or behavioral repertoires are weeded out by natural selection.

In addition, several factors can increase the rate of loss of variation. In particular, inbreeding, or the mating of close relatives, and variation in breeding success between the sexes or among individuals within one sex are significant. Breeding practices that will maximise the genetic variation retained are summarised elsewhere (Frankel and Soule, 1981; Foose *et al.*, 1986; Mace, 1986a).

From this discussion, it is clear that, in general, the larger the founding stock and the larger the population size, the greater the proportion of genetic variation that will be retained. Realistically, there are constraints on these numbers. If we have some idea of the time scale for the project, however, it will be possible to estimate the numbers of animals needed to preserve some predetermined level of genetic variation (Soule *et al.*, 1986; see Figure 8.1).

Figure 8.1: The effective population size required to maintain 90% genetic diversity (measured as heterozygosity) over a 200-year time interval as a function of generation length and the number of founders

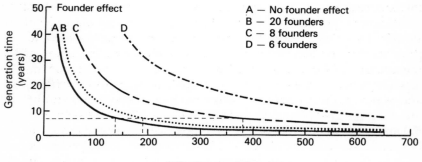

Source: Redrawn from Soule *et al.* (1986)

For many programmes now being organized, a time scale of 200 years has been set (Soule *et al.*, 1986), and, although this is considerably longer than the 25 years we are celebrating at this meeting, it may be a reasonable time scale to aim at, in order to maintain a viable population in captivity to support the re-introduced populations. If there are about 18 unrelated founder animals, a captive population of around 220 individuals will be required to maintain 90% of the genetic variation (measured by heterozygosity) if breeding management is optimal. In fact, it is difficult to achieve optimal management in polygynous species and this value should probably be multiplied by about two to three to give a better estimate of the required number of individuals.

Finally, having established the genetic aims for the programme, and a population size and management protocol which might realistically be expected to achieve these goals, it is important to manage the population for stable size and structure. Populations which fluctuate widely in numbers are not only prone to extinction, but will also lose variation dramatically at each trough in numbers. Populations that are rapidly increasing in size cause all kinds of management difficulties, and solutions that may well be suboptimal in terms of the long-term welfare of the species. In summary, one of the aims of captive-breeding programmes for endangered species such as the Arabian Oryx is to preserve a maximal level of genetic diversity in demographically stable populations.

The Present Status of the Arabian Oryx

I shall now present some data summarising the present status of the Arabian Oryx population worldwide. These analyses are based on the international studbooks which have been produced since 1978 by Dr James Dolan of the San Diego Zoological Society and, prior to that, by the Fauna Preservation Society (FPS). They are remarkably valuable, both for understanding the dynamics of what has happened to the Arabian Oryx populations and for predicting and planning for the future. There are Oryx herds elsewhere that are not documented in the studbooks (Jones, this volume, pp. 47–57) and, as a result, this analysis is not complete. The data are not, however, available on these other herds and therefore they cannot be part of any breeding programme that attempts genetic and demographic management.

From the studbook, we can identify 18 founder animals which, so far as we are aware, are unrelated (Table 8.1. The first three resulted from 'Operation Oryx' (Grimwood, this volume, pp. 1–8) and were joined by the female 'Caroline' from the Zoological Society of London (she was apparently captured in 1958 in Oman). A further two females were offered to FPS (now the Fauna and Flora Preservation Society, FFPS) by Kuwait, but unfortunately one of these died before reaching Phoenix and the other one never bred. Finally, four Oryx from the private collection of the then ruler of Saudi Arabia joined the five animals in Phoenix, and these nine animals were the basis of the World Herd (Grimwood, this volume, pp. 1–8; Homan, this volume, pp. 9–13). The Los Angeles Zoo established a separate herd with animals from Riyadh Zoo, and we assume that these are unrelated to the four presented from Riyadh earlier. The female of this pair arrived at Los Angeles already pregnant by a different male (here called male 'A') and the calf later bred, thereby increasing the number of founder animals. Subsequently, other unrelated individuals have bred and their descendants are living in the population recorded in the international studbook. Other founders have appeared from time to time, but have no living descendants listed in the studbook.

Table 8.1: Founder animals for the studbook population of Arabian Oryx as of 31 December 1985

Studbook No.	Sex		Offspring
1	F	Edith, Wadi Mitan	13
2	M	Tomatum, Wadi Mitan	12
3	M	Pat, Wadi Mitan	13
4	F	Caroline, Oman (ZSL)	9
5	F	Salwa, Kuwait	0
8	F	Lucy, Riyadh	4
9	F	Cuned, Riyadh	8
10	M	Riyadh, Riyadh	8
11	M	Aziz Aziz, Riyadh	0
58	F	Al Shamsi, Riyadh Zoo	5
59	M	Djalal Baha, Riyadh Zoo	43
A	M	? Sire of Studbook No. 60	1
140[a]	M	Antar, Al Areen	2
141[a]	F	Maha, Al Areen	2
189[a]	F	Delilah, Qatar	4
190	F	Jamila, Qatar	2
327[a]	M	Ibn Soora, Al Ain	2
339	F	Jameera, Al Ain	1

Note: a. Living at 31 December 1985.

The latest studbook published (Dolan, 1985) lists over 800 animals, of which 331 were living at the end of 1985. Over a period of 20 years, the population has increased rapidly (Figure 8.2) and the pattern of increase shown is approximately exponential, with the population doubling about every four years (Stanley Price, in press). In fact, the actual growth rate may be slightly higher as there are a number of animals listed in the studbook when born for which subsequent information is missing, and these numbers may therefore sometimes be underestimates. This rapid population

Figure 8.2: History of the Arabian Oryx studbook population

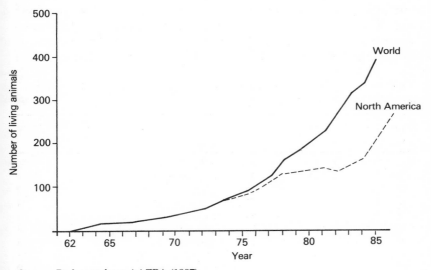

Source: Redrawn from AAZPA (1987)

growth rate has resulted from several factors. First, survival rates have always been high, even in the very early years, when most individuals reached 12 or more years. Figure 8.3 shows survival rates of calves listed in the studbook. The pattern does not differ between the sexes and apart from the first year of life, when mortality approaches 25%, annual mortality up to age eight is about 4% in females and 6% in males. Thereafter, annual mortality is about 9–10% for both sexes, with the oldest individuals surviving to 20 years. There are only three individuals that have survived to over 17 years, so the statistics at this end of the curve are based on rather few data.

Inevitably, with so few founder animals, inbreeding has occurred with increasing frequency over the years. Figure 8.4 shows the average inbreeding coefficient for calves born in each year since

1970. Until 1972 there was no inbreeding—a remarkable testament to the early management regime at Phoenix. Since then, the average annual inbreeding coefficient has increased and recently a

Figure 8.3: Survivorship curves of Arabian Oryx, 1965–85

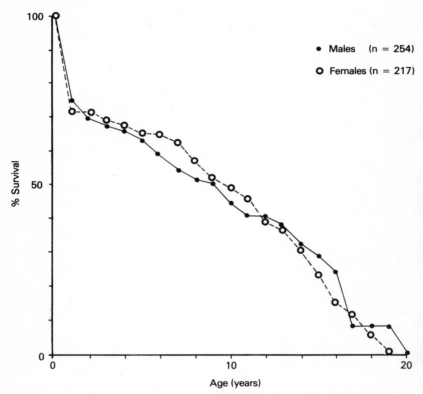

plateau has been attained. This plateau may actually be illusory. In many collections, breeding males are retained with large harems over quite extensive periods of time. Inbreeding coefficients may be quite low, but large numbers of offspring that are closely related result, and these will form the breeding core in the subsequent generations. This in part explains the steep rise between 1975 and 1978. As I have already mentioned, inbreeding should be avoided where possible, as it is one way in which genetic variation is rapidly lost from the population. In addition, in a variety of ungulate species, inbred calves have a higher mortality than noninbred calves (Ralls *et al.*, 1979; Ballou and Ralls, 1982). It seems that there may be a similar phenomenon in the Yalooni herd (Stanley Price, in press and this volume, pp. 18–34). There is no significant effect of inbreeding on survival in the studbook animals, but there are problems in analysing heterogeneous data sets of this sort and this should not necessarily be taken as indicating that inbreeding will have no effect on survival. The pattern of inbreeding over time shows also that there are now fewer and fewer calves which are not inbred, and this is an inevitable consequence of so few unrelated founder animals.

Figure 8.4: Inbreeding in captive populations of Arabian Oryx over time

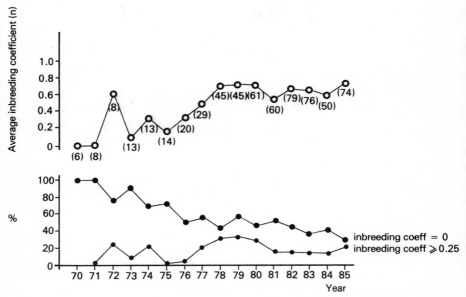

The other way in which herd management will accelerate the rate of loss of genetic diversity is through breeding success being unevenly distributed between males and females (Denniston, 1978; Mace, 1986a). In terms of maintaining genetic diversity, herds would optimally be managed so that each individual produced the same number of surviving offspring. Practically, this may not be at all optimal and attempting to ensure it could greatly upset herd stability and normal behaviour patterns. However, there are clearly instances where single males have been retained as breeding males in large herds over very long periods. Among males, the distribution of breeding success is highly skewed (Figure 8.5), with a few individuals dominating. Of 64 males that have bred, three have sired about 160 calves and one has sired almost 100.

Figure 8.5: Distribution of breeding success in Arabian Oryx (1965–1985)

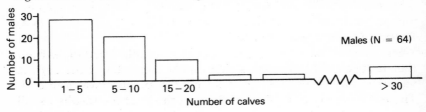

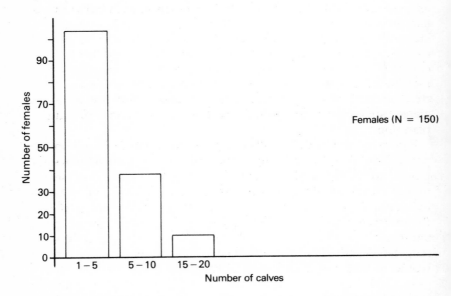

Almost three times as many females as males have bred, which means that there are a lot of males for which there are no descendants and the genetic variation they carry is lost when they die. These kinds of distortions have serious effects on loss of genetic diversity and often result from breeding policies that aim for high rates of calf production. Since another consequence of these practices is a reduction in generation length, which is also undesirable for long-term genetic management, it is important to moderate the variance in breeding success both within and between the sexes.

At the end of 1985, 176:155 Oryx were listed in 28 collections in 14 countries. The majority (220) were in North America, some 40 individuals were found in Europe and North Africa, and the rest were largely in the Middle East (50). The largest single collections are at San Diego (45), International Wildlife Park, USA (43), Phoenix (41) and Shaumari (40).

Since it is possible to reconstruct almost complete pedigrees from the studbooks, it is also possible to make estimates of the genetic variation that has been retained since the population was founded. There is a variety of methods for doing this, but the results I shall present are based on simulations of pedigrees known colloquially as 'genedrops' (MacLuer *et al.*, 1986). In essence, each individual is allocated a unique genotype and, using the pedigree from the studbook, matings are simulated many times over. At the end of each run, the surviving genes in living individuals are scored. The estimates are therefore only approximate, but I think that this method of analysis makes fewer unacceptable assumptions than other methods in complex pedigrees of this sort, and also provides statistics which can be easily interpreted and are useful for future planning.

Figure 8.6 shows the results of a genedrop analysis based on the population recorded as living at the end of 1985. Two statistics are plotted for each founder animal. First, the percentage representation is a measure of the contribution of each founder animal to the living population. The dominant animals are 'Edith' (No. 1), one of the original 'Operation Oryx' females, and the Los Angeles male, studbook number 59. The World Herd animals and the Los Angeles imports dominate. A maximum level of genetic variation would be retained if all founders contributed equally, but this is clearly far from the case. One simple guideline for population management is to breed preferentially from the offspring of the under-represented founders. There are, however, other, perhaps more sophisticated, statistics that can be used. Figure 8.6 also shows estimates of the proportion of each founder's genome that has been lost. From this statistic, we can see some of the remarkable success of the Oryx breeding programme: among the ten major founders, less than 25% of the genome has been lost in all but three animals, and in five of these 4% or less has been lost. One of the reasons for this is the rapid increase in population size in the early years at Phoenix, which resulted in most of the founder animals producing eight or more calves, most of which subsequently bred themselves. Thus, a large proportion of each founder's genome was secured in the population. On the whole, the males had more surviving offspring than the females.

These data were based on the entire international population, but of course the structure of the population differs widely in different areas. Figure 8.7 shows the same data for North America, Europe, and the rest of the world separately. We can see that the North American population most closely resembles the world

Figure 8.6: Genetic structure of the world studbook population of Arabian Oryx as of 31 December 1985. The founder animals are listed by studbook number across the central axis and their representation in the living population is plotted as either percentage representation, or as the estimated proportion of the genome that is lost. See text for further details

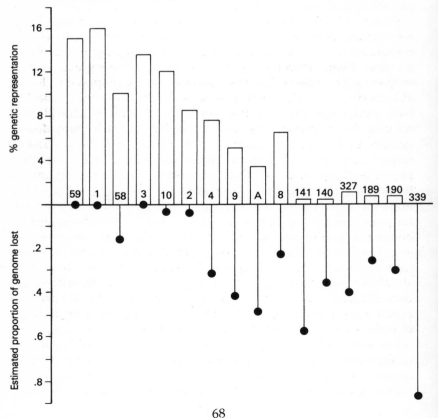

structure, and this is bound to be the case as most individuals are at present in North America. There are, however, a number of striking differences. Four founders are not represented at all in North America and three are represented only outside North America and Europe. The European population is dominated by Founder 1, with two of the founders well represented in North America (58 and 59) contributing relatively little. Finally, Founder 8, from which a rather high proportion has been lost in North America, fares better in Europe because an ancestral lineage that has become extinct in North America persists in Europe. Realistically, management has to be restricted geographically, and there are many advantages in managing one large population as a variety of sub-units (Foose, 1983; Foose *et al.*, 1986). Much, however, can be gained overall by prudent exchange of individuals between different regions. This point is further borne out by one other set of figures which the genedrop analysis can provide.

So far, all the statistics relate to present status and give little information about expected future changes. One statistic which can guide short-term management plans is the proportion of the genome of each founder animal that is still surviving but at low frequency. This may be broadly equated with the proportion that is at high risk of loss, because it persists in only a few individuals. I have chosen a frequency of 0.01 to work with here, which will very roughly be a measure of the proportion of each individual's genome that is present in three or fewer living individuals. These results are plotted in Figure 8.8. In the total international-studbook population, less than 10% is at high risk in each of the ten major founders, but up to 80% in the others. Within the regions, however, the situation is more serious and probably more relevant for population management. It is worth noting that these figures do not necessarily correlate with the proportion of genes surviving (e.g. the founder called 'A'). There are two main points to draw from these data. Firstly, it is possible to identify individuals that should be bred to decrease the risk of losing more genetic variation. Secondly, the poorly represented individuals in one geographical region can be greatly aided by bringing in animals from elsewhere as needs differ between the different populations.

The same principles apply to the re-introduced herd in Oman, where rational selection of individuals to join the herd should consider the genetic and demographic status of the herd, as well as husbandry and veterinary considerations (Mace, 1986b).

Figure 8.7: Genetic structure of studbook populations of Arabian Oryx within North America, Europe, and the rest of the world separately

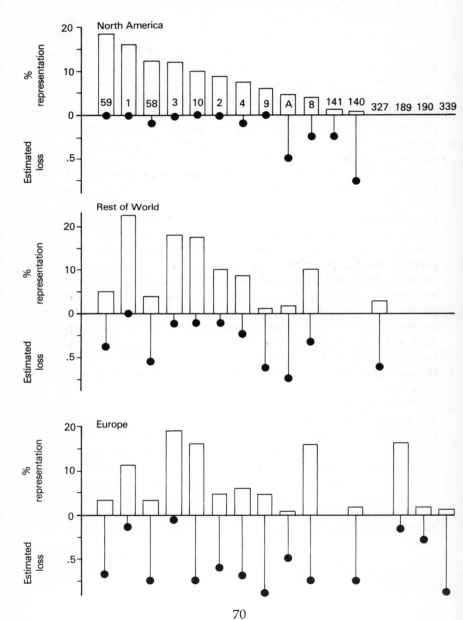

Organisation and Execution of Breeding Programmes

I hope that it has become apparent that to manage the species optimally and to give it the best chance of a long-term future will require management at a level above and beyond what an individual collection can achieve. Although the data I have presented are generally encouraging, and certainly are a testament to those responsible for management in the early years, a few words of caution are appropriate. As we have seen, the population is descended from rather few animals and, as time goes on and the population must stop expanding so quickly, the rate of loss of genetic variation will increase. Along with this, inbreeding co-efficients will inevitably rise and, although this may not seem a serious problem at present, there are a variety of lines of evidence that suggest that it could become more serious. Recent management practices have tended to slow down inbreeding, but could well have a deleterious effect on the next generation, and certainly the greatly biased distribution of male breeding success will contribute significantly to an increased loss of genes in the next few generations. It is probably worth stressing here that the population seems to be doing reasonably well, largely because of the rapid increase in population size. This must slow down over the next few years, and the effects of sub-optimal management will then become more evident. The present is therefore the appropriate time to introduce some kind of management policy for the Oryx, truly in the spirit of 'Operation Oryx' and the World Herd. Rather than being cause for complacency, the re-introduction projects, especially that in Oman, can serve as a focus for such a management programme which should have the twin aims of providing a demographically stable and genetically diverse captive population and producing surplus individuals for re-introduction. There has to be continuing involvement in projects such as the introduction in Oman, both because we expect high mortality and because there may be unforeseen problems, such as certain lineages proving less fit than others. It should be the responsibility of those managing the captive population to ensure that quite precise requests for the re-introduction programmes can be met from the managed population with minimal disruption.

As we have seen, the majority of studbook animals are found in North America and it is here that the population is most stable. So far, a secure population has not been established in Europe. The

71

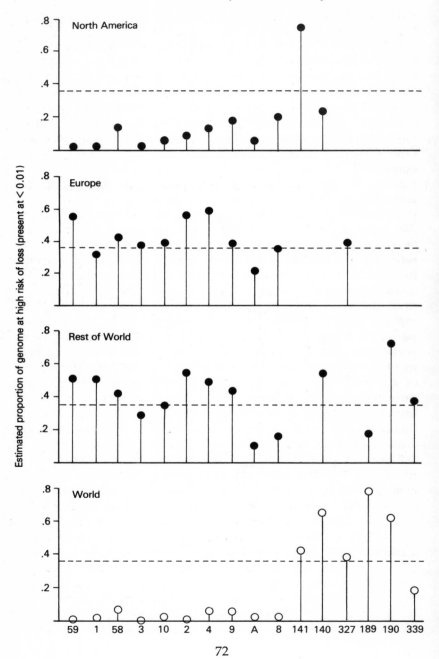

Figure 8.8: The proportion of each founder animal's genome at low frequency (low = .01) and therefore at high risk of loss. The data are analysed independently within each of the major geographical regions, as well as for the population as a whole

North American population at present must therefore bear the brunt of the species' needs. The American Association of Zoological Parks and Aquariums (AAZPA), through its conservation office, has organised a Species Survival Programme (SSP) for the Arabian Oryx since 1981 (AAZPA, 1987), and Dr James Dolan, the international studbook-keeper, is the species co-ordinator. Twenty collections with about 200 animals—the vast majority of the North American population—now participate in the SSP. In March of this year, the SSP group produced a report (AAZPA, 1987) with detailed recommendations for breeding and transfer on an animal-by-animal basis for each of the collections involved, as well as selecting nine animals to be sent to Oman to join the re-introduced herds. Specifically, the SSP aims to manage a population of 350 animals in North America and will attempt to increase the genetic diversity by equalising founder representation, as well as broadening the genetic base by bringing in new founder stock where possible. A programme such as this has many benefits. Each participating institution makes a commitment to species management along the lines recommended by the SSP, with the concerns of the species as a whole as the main priority. The SSP also provides a forum through which requests for animals for re-introduction programmes can be channelled productively, and, finally, it provides a cohesive body with clearly defined aims with which other regional programmes can collaborate.

The European population is small, as yet, but there is a recognised need for co-operative management and all the relevant collections have now expressed their willingness to be involved in a co-operative management programme similar to the AAZPA SSP.

Conclusions

These data on the genetic status of studbook Arabian Oryx are important because this is the population upon which the future of the species, both in the wild and in captivity, still depends. The fact that there are now several hundred animals in captivity and apparently healthy herds in the desert in Oman and Jordan does not guarantee the species a safe future, but should rather serve as a platform from which to launch plans for the next 25 or more years. We must recognise that both captive breeding and re-introduction plans need a long-term commitment with continuous monitoring, re-assessment and replanning if early efforts and endeavours are not to have been in vain.

References

AAZPA (1987) *SSP Masterplan for Arabian Oryx*. American Association of Zoological Parks and Aquariums, Conservation Office, c/o Minnesota Zoo, Apple Valley, Minneapolis, Minnesota.

Ballou, J., and Ralls, K. (1982) Inbreeding and juvenile mortality in small populations of ungulates: a detailed analysis. *Biological Conservation 24*: 239–71.

Denniston, C. (1978) Small population size and genetic diversity: implications for endangered species. In Temple, S.A. (ed.), *Endangered Birds: Management Techniques for Preserving Threatened Species*. University of Wisconsin Press, Madison.

Dolan, J. (1985) *Arabian Oryx Studbook*. Zoological Society of San Diego.

Foose, T. (1983) The relevance of captive populations to the maintenance of biotic diversity. In Schonewald-Cox, C.M., Chambers, S.M., Macbryde, B., and Thomas, L. (eds.), *Genetics and Conservation*. Benjamin Cummings Publishing Co., Menlo Park, California: 374–407.

Foose, T., Lande, R., Flesness, N., Rabb, G., and Read, B. (1986) Propagation Plans. *Zoo Biology 5*: 139–46.

Frankel, O.H., and Soule, M.E. (1981) *Conservation and Evolution*. Cambridge University Press, Cambridge.

Frankham, R., Hemmer, H., Ryder, O.A., Cothran, E.G., Soule, M.E. Murray, N.D., and Snyder, M. (1986) Selection in captive populations. *Zoo Biology 5*: 127–38.

Mace, G.M. (1986a) Genetic management of small populations. *Int. Zoo Ybk. 24/25*: 167–74.

Mace, G.M. (1986b) Status of Arabian Oryx in Captivity. Report for the IUCN/SSC Captive Breeding Specialist Group.

MacLuer, J.W., Vandeburgh, J.L., Read, B., and Ryder, O.A. (1986) Pedigree analysis by computer simulation. *Zoo Biology 5*: 147–60.

Ralls, K., Brugger, K., and Ballou, J. (1979) Inbreeding and juvenile mortality in small populations of ungulates. *Science 206*: 1101–3.

Soule, M., Gilpin, M., Conway, W., and Foose, T. (1986) The millenium ark: how long a voyage, how many staterooms, how many passengers? *Zoo Biology 5*: 101–14.

Stanley Price, M.R. (in press).

9. Veterinary Aspects of the Hippotraginae

Richard A. Kock and Christine M. Hawkey

Introduction

The subfamily Hippotraginae ('horse antelopes') according to Simpson (1945) includes the desert antelopes: Addax *Addax nasomaculatus*, Arabian Oryx *Oryx leucoryx*, Beisa Oryx *O. gazella beisa*, Fringe-eared Oryx *O. g. calotis*, Gemsbok *O. g. gazella* and the Scimitar-horned Oryx *O. dammah*. The Roan Antelope *Hippotragus equinus* and the Sable Antelope *H. niger* are other members of the subfamily inhabiting savanna grasslands, thorn, miambo and coastal fringe habitat (Eltringham, 1979). These hardy species, adapted to desert and semi-arid environments, are now maintained in captivity in zoos and wildlife parks under varying systems of management and climatic conditions throughout the world.

This paper aims to provide basic veterinary information on the Hippotraginae for clinicians and wildlife biologists to enable optimal management.

Clinical Examination and Anaesthesia

These antelopes are difficult and dangerous to restrain manually owing to their aggressive tendencies, large body size and long rapier-like horns. In all but the young and tame, sedation or anaesthesia is required for clinical examination. Immobilisation can be achieved in confinement or under extensive management by remote injection with potent opiate analgesics (etorphine—C-Vet Limited; Carfentanyl—Wildnil, Wildlife Laboratories Inc.) in conjunction with sedatives (xylazine—Rompun—Bayer; acepromazine —marketed with etorphine as Immobilon—C-Vet Limited). The effect of the opiate analgesics can be reversed at the end of the

75

Veterinary Aspects of the Hippotraginae

procedure with the use of diprenorphine (Revivon—C-Vet Limited) or naloxone (narcan—Du Pont UK Limited), as can certain sedatives such as xylazine with the use of alpha-2 agonist antagonists (yohimbine—Antagonil, Wildlife Laboratories Inc; idazoxan and RX 8200100—Reckitt and Coleman Limited). In the authors' experience, etorphine and xylazine is a safe and reliable immobilising combination for any member of the subfamily. The advent of the alpha-2 agonist antagonists allows for higher doses of xylazine to be used,

Table 9.1: Drug dosages for immobilisation of Hippotraginae

	Immobilising Agents – Total Dose (mg)		
	Adult Range		
	Etorphine	+	Xylazine
Addax	1.0 – 4.0		10 – 40
Gemsbok	3.5 – 6.0		20 – 60
Beisa & Fringe-eared Oryx	3.0 – 6.0		20 – 40
Arabian Oryx	1.5 – 4.5		10 – 45
Scimitar-horned Oryx	1.0 – 4.0		10 – 40
Roan Antelope	2.5 – 4.0		5 – 30
Sable Antelope	2.5 – 4.0		5 – 30

General Notes: 1. *Reversing agents.* To reverse the effects of etorphine, it is usual to administer an equal volume of diprenorphine intravenously; this assumes the etorphine is injected at 2.45 mg/ml and the diprenorphine is prepared as 3 mg/ml. To reverse xylazine, an alpha-2 agonist antagonist can be administered intravenously (yohimbine—15 mg total dose; idazoxan—5 mg total dose; or RX 821002—1 mg total dose).
2. *Acepromazine.* This sedative can be administered in conjunction with etorphine (as Immobilon—C-Vet Limited) and xylazine. The total xylazine dose can be reduced by approximately one-third to one-half (Wiesner and van Hegel, 1985).
3. *Ketamine.* This dissociative anaesthetic can be administered at approximately 10–50 mg total dose in conjunction with etorphine and xylazine. Etorphine doses can be reduced by more than 50% (Sylvestris and Heck, 1984).
4. Addax can also be immobilised using 'Telazol' which is a mixture of Tiletamine and Zolazepam at a dose of 700–900 mg. Higher doses are indicated for males and excitable individuals; lower doses for females and tame individuals.
5. Gemsbok can also be immobilised using 2.3–5.0 mg of Carfentanyl with 25 mg of Xylazine.

which ensures a smoother, more rapid induction with good muscle relaxation. Problems reported with the use of etorphine and/or xylazine (Machado *et al.*, 1983) are likely to be due to inadequate dosage or overdosage with inadequate reversal under conditions of climatic stress and/or capture or where repeated doses of neuroleptics are used and animals are excessively fat (pers. obs.). Recent studies (Kock and Pearce, 1985; Pearce and Kock, 1988) indicate that the use of etorphine and xylazine with or without acepromazine in Scimitar-horned Oryx results in a mild hypoxia and hypercapnia. The physiological state induced is reasonably stable except for body temperature, which can decline rapidly. Carfentanyl, Tiletamine and Zolazepam and Ketamine require further evaluation and comparative studies before their use can be fully recommended.

Immobilised animals should wherever possible be kept on their brisket to reduce the likelihood of bloat or regurgitation. For prolonged procedures endotracheal intubation is advisable, as passive regurgitation in an immobilised animal can lead to inhalation pneumonia (Griner, 1983; Pearce *et al.*, 1985). For surgical procedures, gaseous anaesthesia with reversal of the immobilising agents is indicated. Halothane (May and Baker) and methoxyflurane (C-Vet Limited) are suitable agents. Where lateral recumbency is necessary, animals should be stomach-tubed to reduce the likelihood of bloat.

Clinical examination of the Hippotraginae is straightforward. Pulse and respiratory rates are affected by sedation and should not be taken as normal. Body temperature can be markedly elevated by excitation or lowered after immobilisation from rapid radiant heat losses. The possibility exists of a normal fluctuation of body temperature in the desert Hippotraginae, as seen in the Camel, where a variation of 6°C in 24 hours is possible (Higgins and Kock, 1986).

Auscultation is of value, as is abdominal examination, which can include abdominocentesis and rectal palpation. Ultrasonography and radiography are useful diagnostic procedures where facilities allow. Blood samples for clinical pathology are easily obtained from the jugular vein.

Clinical Pathology

Normal haematological values of isolated populations of Hippotraginae are documented (Pospisil *et al.*, 1984; ISIS, 1986). Differences related to sex and age of the animal have been examined in

Veterinary Aspects of the Hippotraginae

the Scimitar-horned Oryx (Brush *et al.*, 1983; Hawkey and Hart, 1984) and in the Arabian Oryx (Bounoies-Dalton and Hood, 1980). Comparative haematology of the Hippotraginae (Hawkey, 1987) demonstrates the similarity among the desert antelopes and the marked differences in red-cell parameters between these and the Roan and Sable Antelopes; haemoglobin levels and red-cell numbers being high and the mean cell volume and mean cell haemoglobin concentration lower in the Roan and Sable Antelopes when compared with the others.

Biochemical composition of Hippotragine blood is comparatively unremarkable, although there is little published information on this (Pospisil *et al.*, 1984; ISIS, 1986). Plasma vitamin E estimations in three collections of ungulates (Brush and Anderson, 1986) provide some useful data.

Parasitic Infections

External and internal parasites can be pathogenic to the host. A number of infections have been reported in Hippotraginae, some of which are potentially debilitating. Among the protozoa, *Cryptosporidia* were recorded in Scimitar-horned Oryx, Fringe-eared Oryx, Addax and Sable Antelope with diarrhoea in captivity (Van Winkle, 1985). The post-mortem examination showed large numbers of *Cryptosporidia* in the small intestine, with little evidence of inflammation; in a number of cases *Salmonella typhimurium* was isolated from faeces. The large numbers of *Cryptosporidia* were considered to be an initiating factor for the diarrhoea and associated with colostrum deprivation and over-crowding. The disease is considered to be self-limiting in ruminants. In ten years at The Zoological Society of London, herds of Scimitar-horned Oryx, Gemsbok, Roan Antelope, Addax and Arabian Oryx have had regular faecal analysis, and only on two occastions have *Coccidia* been identified and at no time have *Cryptosporidia* been seen.

Serological evidence for infection with *Babesia* and *Theileria* were demonstrated in Sable Antelope in southern Africa (Wilson *et al.*, 1968). The clinical significance of these findings is debatable, although mortality has been recorded in Roan Antelope from these protozoa. In this same survey, antibodies to *Anaplasma* were recorded, but it is a rare finding in indigenous antelopes. *Anaplasma marginale* caused severe anaemia requiring blood transfusions in two captive Addax (Ebedes and Reyer, 1982), and the

78

possibility of this species and other Hippotraginae being carriers exists. These blood parasites require the tick as an intermediate host. Hippotraginae previously unexposed to these blood parasites may be at risk, particularly when stressed (Grootenhuis, 1979).

Helminthic parasites are commonly found in grazing species of ungulates, but desert antelopes in their natural habitat are unlikely to be exposed to a significant degree. Hippotraginae maintained in captivity carry the local helminth parasites and usually carry heavier burdens. These may be pathogenic owing to an inability of these species to mount an effective immune response (Kock, 1983).

Clinical cysticercosis caused by the tapeworm *Cysticercus tenuicollis* was recorded in a Beisa Oryx (Arora *et al.*, 1984), and lesions were noted in the brain, mesentery and peritoneal cavity.

A lungworm *Parelaphostrongylus tenuis* was recorded in a Sable Antelope and possibly in a Scimitar-horned Oryx in herds at Front Royal, Virginia, USA (Nichols *et al.*, 1986). In these cases, transmission was through biting flies, most probably from local White-tailed Deer *Odocoileus virginianus* populations which were the host species in the region. This nematode affects the central nervous system and is difficult to treat.

Nematodes recorded at The Zoological Society of London include *Trichuris* spp., *Nematodirus* spp. and *Trichostrongyle* spp. Parasitic gastro-enteritis has been a major disease problem in Hippotraginae at Whipsnade Park Zoo, particularly in neonates, juveniles or stressed individuals (Kock, 1983). A prophylactic anthelmintic programme using benzimadazoles (Panacur—Hoechst UK) and ivermectin (Ivomec—Mercke, Sharpe & Doehme) in conjunction with careful management to reduce stress has proved to be successful. Trichuriasis was noted to be a problem at the San Diego Zoo in certain Hippotraginae (Griner, 1983).

Ecto-parasites seen in Hippotraginae include mites, lice, ticks, fleas and their larvae, although local conditions will dictate which ecto-parasites affect Hippotraginae in any particular environment. The importance of ticks and flying insects as 'worrying agents' and in transmission of blood parasites and viruses in certain localities should not be underestimated. Under ranch conditions at Galana in Kenya, ticks on Beisa Oryx were found to be small in number and without ill effects (Thresher, 1980), an advantage in ranching this species when compared with cattle in the area. Tick toxicosis as a cause of mortality in wild ungulates has not been proven, but secondary infection of tick-bite lesions, especially with maggots, has been known to cause the deaths of Sable Antelope in Zimbabwe (Lightfoot and Norval, 1980). Host resistance to tick infestations is well recognised (Norval, 1975), and certain Hippotraginae may be more susceptible than some other antelopes, especially when stressed by over-crowding or a heavy tick challenge (Grobler and Charsley, 1978; Lightfoot and Norval, 1980). This may be a result of their natural dispersal characteristics and habitat where tick challenge would be minimal.

Chorioptes bovis, a mange mite, was found to be the cause of a crusting dermatitis (affecting the head and limbs) in the Whipsnade Park herd of Scimitar-horned Oryx. Treatment with ivermectin (Ivomec—Mercke, Sharpe & Doehme) appears to be effective in controlling the condition.

Infectious Diseases — Viruses, Bacteria, Fungi

A number of viruses are known to affect the Hippotraginae in common with many other ruminant species. Foot-and-mouth, a virus disease, has been recorded in Sable Antelope in southern Africa but the diagnosis was established purely on the observation of lesions and evidence of an epizootic (Rossiter and Albertyn, 1947). Isolation of the virus has not been reported from any Hippotragine suspected to date, although the response of some species to foot-and-mouth disease vaccination was examined (Hedger *et al.*, 1980). Blue-tongue virus was isolated from an Addax in the USA (Ramsey and Baumeister, 1983) and also in Sable Antelope (Griner, 1983).

Virus-neutralising antibodies to malignant catarrhal-fever virus (African form) were found in serum samples from 50 Beisa Oryx in Kenya (Mushi and Karstad, 1981), and a serological survey using immunofluorescence testing (Reid, 1987) showed high titres recorded in Scimitar-horned Oryx kept at Whipsnade Park. The possibility of a malignant catarrhal-fever carrier state in the Hippotraginae needs further investigation (Barnard, 1984). Sable Antelope at least are also susceptible to epizootic haemorrhagic disease (Griner and Nelson, 1970).

Another virus, peste de petites ruminants, was reported at Al Ain Zoo in the United Arab Emirates (Furley *et al.*, 1987) and resulted in the death of a Gemsbok, but other Hippotraginae in the collection, including Arabian Oryx and Scimitar-horned Oryx, were unaffected. Panzootics and epidemics of rinderpest virus in Africa involved Hippotraginae (Scott, 1981), but no cases were proven by virus isolation. There is serological evidence of infection with rinderpest virus in Beisa Oryx (Rossiter *et al.*, 1983), but their importance as a host for rinderpest in domestic stock is not known. Investigation into the prevalence of antibodies to parainfluenza-3 virus in wildlife in Kenya found (Nyaga *et al.*, 1981) two *Oryx* (spp.) sera to be negative by HI tests in areas where other species of ungulates, including domestic cattle, were found to be positive.

As more investigations of diseases in Hippotraginae are undertaken, the list of viruses found to infect them will undoubtedly grow. From the available evidence, it would appear that the desert antelopes are not exceptionally susceptible to infection with viruses commonly seen in Bovidae. This may in part be due to the small populations of these species in captivity and in the wild and their relative isolation from domestic stock.

Bacterial disease can be a significant cause of mortality, particularly in young animals. In adults, bacteria frequently cause chronic disease which can be insidious in onset. *Mycobacterium tuberculosis* was diagnosed in two Beisa Oryx at post-mortem examination (Lomme *et al.*, 1978), with lesions affecting lungs, liver, uterus and mediastinal lymph nodes, but no obvious clinical signs other than weight loss. It is interesting to note that only one of these two animals responded positively to a tuberculin skin test.

Nocardiosis has been recorded in Addax (Ayers and Griner, 1971). This disease can be confused with tuberculosis as the organism is partly positive Ziel Nielsen staining. The disease in the Addax was an acute fulminating condition with diarrhoea. Lesions were found in the lungs, liver and on the parietal surfaces.

Pseudotuberculosis (*Yersinia pseudotuberculosis*) was recorded in a Sable Antelope (Kollias and Peyton, 1983) and in a neonatal Scimitar-horned Oryx at Whipsnade Park Zoo. Rodents and birds are potential sources of this infection and it was notable in the case of the Scimitar-horned Oryx neonate that this animal was closely confined as a result of being winter-born (it is the usual practice to ensure that calves are born only in spring and summer). *Corynebacterium pyogenes* and *Fusiformis necrophorum* were isolated from abscesses in the liver of a Roan Antelope in Europe (Jedlicke, 1981), and *C. pyogenes* was considered the cause of a pneumonia in a Scimitar-horned Oryx which died at Whipsnade. Anthrax was recorded in Roan and Sable Antelope in southern Africa (Nietz,

1965). Anthrax immunisation was attempted in Roan Antelope in Kruger National Park (De Vos *et al.*, 1973).

A variety of bacteria have been incriminated in common diseases such as omphalophlebitis (Griner, 1983), particularly in neonates. No cases of brucellosis, salmonellosis, Johnes disease, pasteurellosis or clostridial disease have been reported in Hippotraginae. It is highly unlikely that the Hippotraginae are not susceptible to these and other bacteria affecting ruminants in general, but the diagnosis and treatment of all these conditions can be approached in a conventional manner.

No fungal diseases have been recorded from Hippotraginae to date. A recent case of mycosis was seen in an Arabian Oryx at the London Zoo and *Absidia* spp. were isolated from a lesion in the cerebral cortex.

Reproduction and Associated Disorders

Examination of the reproductive tract in the female requires immobilisation. The ovaries and uterus can be palpated per rectum in fully grown adult females. Blood samples can be taken for oestrogen and progesterone assays and ultrasonography can be used to examine ovaries and uterus and for pregnancy diagnosis. In the male, the penis and testes can be examined easily. Electro-ejaculation appears to be straightforward: it is reported in the Sable Antelope (Merilan *et al.*, 1982) and recent attempts in the Gemsbok at the Institute of Zoology, London, proved successful. Cryopreservation techniques for Gemsbok sperm were also established. Superovulation and embryo transfer were undertaken in the Scimitar-horned Oryx (Schmidt, 1986) using techniques similar to those used in cattle, but as yet no viable calves have been born.

Infertility is not reported in the Hippotraginae. A recent case at Whipsnade with cystic ovarian disease (luteinising cyst) was treated with prostaglandins apparently successfully, with a return to normal ovarian activity. Overt oestrus behaviour was detected two days after the administration of prostaglandins (Estrumate—Coopers).

Perinatal disorders include still births, abortions and neonatal death. Arabian Oryx in the Phoenix herd suffered 17 neonatal deaths and three still births out of 129 births; the Los Angeles herd suffered 11 neonatal deaths and three still births out of 70 births (Thomas *et al.*, 1986). Dystokia in a Gemsbok has been reported

(Griner, 1983), and occurred in a Scimitar-horned Oryx at Whip-snade post-immobilisation. A caesarian section in the latter case was straightforward and subsequent births were uncomplicated.

The Hippotraginae appear to be reproductively aseasonal; calving intervals are approximately 280 days (Furley and Hunt, 1987). Females are sexually mature at approximately 18 months. In cold-temperate climates, it is advisable to restrict the calving period to the spring and summer to reduce the effects of winter stress on survival. In order to achieve this, it is necessary to separate the male from the herd except for a period of approximately three months during late summer.

Care must be taken in the last trimester of pregnancy to avoid sedation with xylazine, as this drug is potentially an abortifacient.

Surgical Conditions

Hoof and horn disorders are the most common surgically correctable condition seen in captivity. The desert Hippotraginae are particularly susceptible to hoof overgrowth when maintained on pasture, especially where there are high-quality diets. Horn repair has been described (Budiarso, 1971) and is particularly advisable where there is a chronic proliferative reaction to horn fracture or damage.

Traumatic injury is common in Hippotraginae owing to their aggressive tendencies, so poke wounds and lacerations are not infrequent. Treatment of these can be undertaken in a conventional manner. Dislocation of the shoulder in an Oryx was successfully treated by resection of the humeral head (Tadmore, 1980).

A high incidence of bone disease has been reported (Anderson, 1983) and described as osteopetrosis. This can lead to a number of complications.

Where trauma is a particular problem, the management of the herd should be examined — for example, the number of males retained with the females. In general, the Hippotraginae in captivity should be managed as a herd consisting of several females and a single breeding male. Young males must be removed before one year of age. Bachelor groups are difficult to maintain without fighting and stress, except perhaps under very extensive conditions. The Roan Antelope is a possible exception, where there is a questionable territoriality (Eltringham, 1979) and bachelor herds can be successfully managed. Maintaining pairs of Hippotraginae can result in unnecessary stress on the female, poor fertility and possibly injuries. Under ranch management at Galana, the optimal herd size for Beisa Oryx was found to be fewer than 50 animals, above which the social organisation deteriorated (Thresher, 1980).

Nutrition

The Hippotraginae are grazing ruminants and the only predominantly grass-eating antelopes to occupy arid zones (Hofmann, 1973). They are roughage-eaters and relatively non-selective (Eltringham, 1979). Recent studies on the nutrition of Scimitar-horned Oryx (King and Miller, 1983) showed an increased digestibility of all the dietary components examined in this species compared with sheep as a result of increased retention time in the rumen. It was found under experimental conditions that the adult male could maintain constant body weight on 3 kilos of lucerne hay per day.

Behaviourally, the antelopes were found to select out coarser fibrous material. One case of nutritional myopathy occurred during a feeding trial (King and Miller, 1983), and adequate levels of vitamins, particularly A and E, should be fed to Hippotraginae on dry forage rations. Feeding of the Hippotraginae in captivity is straightforward, although obesity can occur in the desert antelopes where excessive grain or concentrated rations are fed, because of their specialised ability to lay down large fat reserves. Expected body weights of neonatal and adult Hippotraginae are shown in Table 9.2.

Table 9.2: Average body weights (kg) of Hippotraginae

| Species | Adult | | Neonate | |
	Male	Female	Male	Female
Gemsbok	250	150	−	
Beisa and Fringe-eared Oryx	200	100	−	
Arabian Oryx	100	90	−	
Scimitar-horned Oryx	150	120	9	10
Roan Antelope	300	150	−	
Sable Antelope	250	150	12	16
Addax	100	50	7.5	5.5

Sources: ZSL, unpubl; Dittrich, 1967; Fowler, 1986.

Hand-rearing of neonatal Scimitar-horned Oryx has been described (Mayar, 1983). Neonatal diarrhoea is not uncommon in hand-reared animals and mother-reared Oryx also suffer from this where the dam and neonate are confined together off pasture. There is some evidence of a difference in milk quality from grass-fed Scimitar-horned Oryx and those on synthetic diets, which may in part explain neonatal diarrhoea (Jones, 1979). Blood dyscrasias and hypovitaminosis E are seen in some of these young animals, and the condition can be fatal without intensive care.

Other digestive disorders reported include bloat in Fringe-eared Oryx, abomasal impaction in the Gemsbok and pancreatic atrophy in Addax (Griner, 1983). Diabetes mellitus with pancreatic atrophy was diagnosed in oryx by Erkin (1972).

Proliferative Diseases

Lymphosarcoma was diagnosed in an Arabian Oryx, and benign haemangiomas found in a Fringe-eared Oryx and a Sable Antelope (Griner, 1983).

Miscellaneous Disorders

Stress can result in weight loss and diarrhoea in all age groups. This can be induced by maintaining groups of male Hippotraginae together as a bachelor herd in confinement. Congenital anomalies have been reported in the Addax and Sable Antelope (Griner, 1983).

Conclusions

1. Veterinary problems of the subfamily Hippotraginae are not exceptional. Immobilisation and anaesthesia is straightfoward so long as specific protocols are adhered to. Clinical examination is uncomplicated and can be approached in a similar manner to that for conventional domestic ruminants.

2. Physiological parameters measured under sedation should be interpreted with care. The animal's body size allows the use of radiography and ultrasonography for diagnostic purposes.

3. Interpretation of clinical pathology can be done with reference to normal values. There are significant differences in this subfamily from other Bovidae, whether domestic or non-domestic.

4. The desert Hippotraginae appear to be more susceptible to helminthic infection when compared with temperate species on grass pasture. This can be controlled with the correct anthelmintic usage and herd management.

5. There appears to be no unusual susceptibility to ecto-parasites or infectious diseases. Tick infestation may be an exception to this in Sable Antelope.

6. Breeding of Hippotraginae in captivity is relatively uncomplicated. Manipulative procedures, including artificial insemination and embryo transfer, appear to be a possibility.

7. The most common disorders of the Hippotraginae are likely to be due to traumatic incidents, usually the result of an imbalanced sex ratio or over-crowding, whether confined intensively or extensively. The long horns are particularly susceptible to damage.

8. Regular hoof care is required with desert antelopes maintained on grass pastures.

9. The Hippotraginae are grazing ruminants and diets similar to those used for domestic bovids are applicable. Care must be taken to avoid obesity as the desert Hippotraginae in particular are able to lay down fat reserves, a characteristic which enables them to tolerate colder conditions than many other African antelopes.

10. The potential for maintaining and breeding the Hippotraginae in captivity throughout the world is good, especially with extensive systems of management.

References

Anderson, M.P. (1983) Preliminary observation of bone disease in Hippotraginae. *Proc. Amer. Assoc. Zoo Vet. Tampa, Florida*: 103.

Arora, B.M., Varna, J.K., Tewari, H., and Mandal, C.K. (1984) Cysticercosis caused by *Cysticercus tenuicollis* in a Beisa Oryx. *Vet. Rec. 114* (8): 197.

Ayers, K.M., and Griner, L.A. (1971) Disseminated nocardiosis in a North African antelope. *J.A.V.M.A. 159*: 611–13.

Barnard B.J.H. (1984) Transmitters and potential transmitters of malignant catarrhal fever. *Proc. 13th World Congress on Diseases of Cattle, Durban, South Africa 1*: 56–60.

Bounoies-Dalton, D., and Hood, H.B. (1980) Haematological values for neonatal Arabian oryx (*Oryx leucoryx*). *J. Zoo Med. 11*: 118–19.

Brush, P.J., and Anderson, P.H. (1986) Levels of plasma a. tocopherol in zoo animals. *Inter. Zoo Ybk 24/25*: 316–21.

Veterinary Aspects of the Hippotraginae

Budiarso, I.T. (1971) Horn repair in a Sable antelope. *J. Zoo An. Med.* 2: 16.

Bush, M., Custer, R.S., Whitia, J.C., and Montali, P.J. (1983) Haemato-logic and serum chemistry values of captive Scimitar-horned oryx (*Oryx tao*). *J. Zoo An. Med.* 14: 51–5.

De Vos, V. (1978) A new potent analgesic for chemical immobilisation of Gemsbok (*Oryx gazella gazella*). *Koedoe* 21: 173–80.

De Vos, V., Vanroozen, G.L., and Kloppers, J.J. (1973) Anthrax immunisation of free ranging Roan antelope (*Hippotragus equinus*) in the Kruger National Park. *Koedoe* 16: 11–25.

Dittrich, L. (1969) Birth weights and weight increases of African antelope born at Hanover Zoo. *Inter. Zoo Ybk* 9: 118–20.

Ebedes, H., and Reyer, F. (1982) Anaplasmosis in two captive Addax (*Addax nasomaculatus*). *Proc. 4th International Conference of Wildlife Diseases Association, Sydney, Australia* 15: 121–4.

Eltringham, S.K. (1979) *The Ecology and Conservation of Large African Mammals.* Macmillan Press, London: pp. 62, 160, 214–16.

Erkin, A.H.M. (1972) Glykosuriemit Pankreasrophei bei Antilopen im Amsterdamen Tiergarten. *Natura Artes magistra Einige Kleniche und Pathologia Aspekta XIV* VISZ: 358–88.

Fowler, M.E. (1986) *Zoo and Wild Animal Medicine.* 2nd Ed. W.B. Saunders Co., London: pp. 942–52.

Furley, C.W., and Hunt, D.W. (1987) Seasonal breeding in some ungulate species. In prep.

Furley, C.W., Taylor, W.P., and Olu, T.U. (1987) An outbreak of peste de petites ruminants in a zoological collection. *Vet. Rec.* in press.

Griner, L.A. (1983) *Pathology of Zoo Animals.* Zool. Soc. of San Diego; p. 546.

Griner, L.A., and Nelson, L.S. (1970) Haemorrhagic disease in exotic ruminants in a zoo. *J.A.V.M.A.* 157: 600–3.

Grobler, J.H., and Charsley, G.W. (1978) Population dynamics in Sable in Rhodesia. Unpublished PhD Thesis, Univ. of Rhodesia: p. 342.

Grootenhuis, J.G. (1979) Theileriosis in wild bovidae in Kenya with special reference to the Eland. PhD Thesis, State Univ. of Utrecht.

Hawkey, C.M. (1987) Unpublished Zoological Society of London data.

Hawkey, C.M., and Hart, M.G. (1984) Age-related changes in the blood count of Scimitar-horned oryx (*Oryx tao*). *J. Zoo An. Med.* 15: 157–60.

Hedger, R.S., Condy, J.B., and Gradwell, D. (1980) The response of some African wildlife species to foot and mouth disease vaccination. *J. Wildlife Diseases* 16 (3): 431–8 (16 ref.).

Higgins, A.J., and Kock, R.A. (1986) A guide to the chemical restraint, clinical examination and medication of the Camel. In Higgins, A.J. (ed.), *The Camel in Health and Disease.* Balliere and Tindall, London: pp. 21–41.

Hofmann, R.R. (1973) The ruminant stomach. *East African Monographs in Biology,* Vol. 2. E. Afr. Lit. Bur: p. 226.

ISIS (1986) *Normal Physiological Data.* N.R. Flesness, Minnesota, USA.

Veterinary Aspects of the Hippotraginae

Jedlicke, P. (1981) *Corynebacterium* and *Fusiformis necrophorum* in Roan antelope. *23rd Int. Symposium on Diseases of Zoo and Wild Animals, Halle/Saale.* Ippen, R. (ed.), Acad. Verlag, Berlin: p. 345.

Jones, D.M. (1979) Vet. clinical report. *J. Zool. Lond.* (1982) *197* (24): 53–4.

King, C.H., and Miller, E.L. (1983) Digestibility and rate of passage of digestion in Oryx and Sheep. Unpubl. Dept Applied Biol., Univ. Cambridge.

Kock, R.A. (1983) Review of Nematode parasites and anthelmintic usage in ungulates at Whipsnade Zoo, The Zoological Society of London. *British Vet. Soc. Newsletter 17* (1983): 7–11.

Kock, R.A., and Pearce, P.C. (1985) Anaesthesia in zoo ungulates. *J. Assoc. Vet. Anaes. 13*: 59–89.

Kollias, G.V., and Peyton, L. (1983) Medical and surgical management of Corynebacterium Pseudotuberculosis infection in a Sable antelope (*Hippotragus niger*). *Proc. Amer. Assoc. Zoo Vet. Tampa, Florida*: p. 101.

Lightfoot, C.J., and Norval, R.A.I. (1980) Tick problems in wildlife in Zimbabwe. *South Afr. J. Wildlife Res. 11* (2): 41–5.

Lomme, J.R., Thoen, C.O., and Hine, E.M. (1978) Mycobacterium Tuberculosis in Oryx. In Montali, R.J. (ed.), *Mycobacterial Infections of Zoo Animals.* Proc. Symp. of Nat. Zool. Park, Smithsonian Inst. Press, Washington D.C.

Machado, C.R., Furley, C.W., and Hood, H. (1983) Observation on the use of M99, Immobilon and Xylazine in the Arabian Oryx (*Oryx leucoryx*). *J. Zoo An. Med. 14*: 107–10.

Mayar, J. (1983) Hand rearing an orphaned Scimitar-horned Oryx (*Oryx tao*). *Inter. Zoo Ybk 23*: 243–8.

Merilan, C.P., Read, B.W., and Boever, W.J. (1982) Semen collection procedure for captive wild animals. *Inter. Zoo Ybk 22*: 241–4.

Mushi, E.Z., and Karstad, L. (1981) Prevalence of virus neutralising antibodies to malignant catarrhal fever virus in oryx (*Oryx beisa calotis*). *J. Wildl. Dis. 17* (3): 467–70.

Nichols, D.K., Montali, R.J., Phillips, L.G., Alvarado, T.P., Bush, M., and Collins, L. (1986) *Parelaphostrongylus tenuis* in captive Reindeer and Sable antelope. *J.A.V.M.A. 188* (6): 619–21.

Nietz, W.O. (1965) A check list and host list of zoonoses occurring in mammals and birds in South and South West Africa. *Ondersterpoort J. Vet. Res. 32*: 189–374.

Norval, R.A.I. (1975) Host-tick interaction. A Review. *Proc. Int. Congress Ent. Soc. Sth Afr.*: pp. 195–201.

Nyaga, P.N., Kaminjolo, J.S., Gathuma, J.M., Omuse, J.K., Nderu, F.M.K., and Gicho, J.N. (1981) Prevalence of antibodies to para influenza-3 virus in various wildlife species and indigenous cattle sharing the same habitat in Kenya. *J. Wildl. Dis. 17* (4): 605–8.

Pearce, P.C., Knight, J.A., Hutton, R.A., Pugsley, S.L., and Hawkey, C.M. (1985) Disseminated intravascular coagulation associated with inhalation

Veterinary Aspects of the Hippotraginae

pneumonitis in Scimitar-horned oryx (*Oryx tao*). *Vet. Rec. 116* (7): 189–90.

Pearce, P.C., and Kock, R.A. (1988) The physiological effects of Etorphine, Acepromazine and Xylazine on the Scimitar-horned oryx (*Oryx tao*). *Res. Vet. Sci.* in prep.

Pospisil, J., Kase, F., Vahala, J., and Moluchova, I. (1984) Basic haematological values in Antelopes. A comparison and concluding remarks. *Comp. Bioc. Physiol. 4*: 815–21.

Ramsey, E.C., and Baumeister, B.M. (1983) Blue Tongue infection in a herd of Addax. *Proc. Amer. Assoc. Zoo Vet. Tampa, Florida*: pp. 73–6.

Reid, H. (1987) in prep. Moredun Institute, Scotland, UK.

Rossiter, L.W., and Albertyn, A.N.E. (1947) Foot and Mouth Disease in Sable. *J.S. Afr. Vet. Med. Assoc. 18*: 16–19.

Rossiter, P.B., Karstad, L., Jenett, D.M., Yamamoto, T., Dardiri, A.H., and Mushi, E.Z. (1983) Neutralising antibodies to rinderpest virus in wild animal sera collected in Kenya between 1970–1981. *Preventative Vet. Med. 1* (3): 257–64.

Schmidt, D.L. (1986) Non-surgical embryo transfer in Scimitar-horned oryx (*Oryx tao*). *Proc. Amer. Assoc. Zoo Vet., Chicago, Illinois*: pp. 10–11.

Scott, G.R. (1981) Rinderpest. In Davis, J.W., Karstad, L.H., and Trainer, D.O. (eds.), *Infectious Diseases of Wild Mammals*. Iowa State Univ. Press, Ames, Iowa: pp. 20–35.

Simpson, G.G. (1945) Principles of classification and classification of the mammals. *Bull. Ass. Mus. Nat. Hist. 85*: 1–350.

Sylvestris, R., and Heck, H. (1984) Further experiments for immobilisation at Catskill Game Farm. *Zool. Garten NF Jena 54* (1/2): 46–8.

Tadmore, A. (1980) Resection of the head of the humerus in an Oryx. *J.A.V.M.A. 177* (9): 949.

Thomas, W.D., Barnes, R., Crotty, M., and Jones, M. (1986) An historical overview of selected rare ruminants in captivity. *Inter. Zoo Ybk 24/25*: 92–3.

Thresher, P. (1980) The economics of domesticated Oryx compared with that of cattle. *World Anim. Review 36*: 37–43.

Van Winkle, T.J. (1985) Cryptosporidiosis in young Artiodactyls. *J.A.V.M.A. 187* (11): 1170–2.

Wallach J.D., and Boever, W.J. (1983) *Diseases of Exotic Animals*. W.B. Saunders Co.: pp. 219–29.

Wiesner, H., and van Hegel, G. (1985) Praktische Hinweise zur Immobilisation von Wild and Zootieren. *Tierärztle Prax. 13*: 113–27.

Wilson, D.E., Bartsch, R.C., Bigalke, E.D., and Thomas, S.E. (1968) Observation on mortality rates and disease in Roan and Sable antelope on nature reserves in the Transvaal. *H. S. Afr. W. Ammgment Assoc. 4*: 203–6.

10. Chemical Immobilisation of Arabian Oryx

*M.H. Woodford, R.A. Kock, R.H. Daly, M.R. Stanley Price,
J. Kidner, J.H. Usher-Smith, and K.A. Emanuelson*

Abstract

The narcotic analgesic, etorphine, in combination with the sedative, xylazine, administered by remote-injection techniques produces a satisfactory immobilisation of Arabian Oryx *Oryx leucoryx*
for routine veterinary procedures. Higher doses of etorphine and
xylazine are necessary in unconfined animals in open paddocks or
wild animals on desert ranges as compared with confined captive
animals. The dose of xylazine is critical for field immobilisation.
The physiological response to these drugs is not adverse and, so
long as normal anaesthetic protocols for ruminants are adhered to,
sedation is a safe procedure. Recovery appears to be prolonged
where high doses of the drug are used (etorphine, more than 0.062
mg/kg; and xylazine, more than 0.8 mg/kg) and inadequate doses
of antagonists administered. Fat animals appear to suffer a long
recovery, with a semi-narcotised state evident for many hours or
even days.

Introduction

The chemical immobilisation of members of a rare and endangered
species can be hazardous, particularly so when there are few
published records of drug dosages and reactions. It is well recognised that the plane of narcosis required, the intervention to be
performed and the circumstances under which the immobilisation
is carried out can all influence the choice of the drugs and doses
employed. The Arabian Oryx is a case in point.

This species was reported extinct in the wild in 1972. Since then
the World Wildlife Fund (WWF), The Fauna and Flora Preservation
Society (FFPS), The International Union for Conservation of

90

Nature (IUCN) and HM Sultan Qaboos bin Said of Oman have combined to carry out the re-introduction of captive herds into the Jiddat-al-Harasis, an area of central Oman in which the last wild Arabian Oryx lived. In addition to this, several Gulf states have developed captive-breeding programmes so that the population in the Middle East now approaches 500. Outside the Middle East, the World Herd, set up in Phoenix, Arizona, and founded by a group caught in the wild in 1962 plus various individuals from zoos and private collections, has provided the animals for re-introduction. Other offspring are now distributed throughout the international zoo community and, as the population grows, the frequency of the need for sedation will increase. To date there is only one report on the use of immobilising agents in Arabian Oryx (Machado *et al.*, 1983), although there are a number of reviews on the use of these agents in ungulates (Jones, 1972, 1977; Harthoorn, 1976; Wiesner *et al.*, 1982; Kock and Pearce, 1985). Doses for Hippotragines are listed in zoo medicine texts (Wallach and Boever, 1983; Fowler, 1986), and a study of the physiological effects of etorphine/acepromazine and xylazine in Scimitar-horned Oryx has been reported (Pearce and Kock, 1988). Anaesthetic complications associated with these agents in Oryx have been reported (Machado *et al.*, 1983; Pearce *et al.*, 1985; Kock, 1988). Machado *et al.* (1983) noted a number of problems in animals immobilised in the Gulf states and in Phoenix, Arizona. These included excitability during induction with etorphine alone (C-Vet Limited) or in combination with acepromazine (Immobilon LA—C-Vet Limited), leading to hyperthermia and traumatic injuries. A prolonged recovery with xylazine (Rompun-Bayer) alone or in combination with etorphine with or without acepromazine has also led to traumatic injuries. The use of these agents on 16 Arabian Oryx from herds in Oman, Saudi Arabia and at the Zoological Society of London's collection at Whipsnade Park, England, on a number of occasions is reported here.

Materials and Methods

In Oman, the Oryx were sedated for attachment with radio collars. The method used was to habituate the Oryx to the presence of a person with a dart pistol (Dist-Inject with automatic syringes and 20 millimetres barbed needles with an effective range of 15 metres). Prior to the actual darting, habituation of the animals to these

91

conditions ensured that they were not stressed before immobilisation.

In Saudi Arabia, the animals were either ill and requiring immediate attention and/or needed to be darted in what was effectively open range prior to penning for translocation. A long-range projector rifle with metal darts (Dist-Inject Model 50) was used, with a range of up to 50 metres. The animals were generally in a flight response and relatively excited when darted. To reduce the risks of hyperthermia caused by high ambient day temperatures in Oman and Saudi Arabia, darting was performed in the early morning. The Oryx at Whipsnade Park Zoo were confined in pens and were immobilised using a blowpipe (Telinject) with plastic darts. Stress to the animals was thus minimised. All the Oryx in this series were immobilised using a combination of etorphine and xylazine. Clinical and anaesthetic details are recorded in Table 10.1 (a, b).

After darting, further disturbance was kept to a minimum and animals were observed from a discrete distance until they were in sternal recumbency. In most instances a cloth was then placed over the head to reduce visual stimulus, and the individuals were maintained in sternal recumbency if at all possible. When in lateral recumbency for any period, the Oryx were intubated with 12–14 millimetres cuffed endotracheal tubes (Arnolds) and a stomach tube placed in the rumen to prevent bloat. At the end of the procedure, reversing agents (diprenorphine and an alpha-2 agonist antagonist, Table 10.1 (b)) were administered and the tubes were removed at the appropriate time. The animals were then kept under observation until normal locomotion and behaviour resumed. At Whipsnade, the physiology of the sedated individuals was monitored. Respiration, heart rates, electrocardiographs, mean systematic arterial pressures and rectal temperatures were recorded using an Albury instrument LT 24 patient monitor with an Amed 2300 pressure transducer, recording on a Schiller Cardovit 3 electrocardiograph. The ECG was recorded on lead 1 (LA sternum, RA last rib left side, LL left rear leg). Arterial pressure lines were maintained with 18-gauge bevelled needles placed in superficial metacarpal or metatarsal arteries with a continuous flush technique with heparinised saline. Blood gas samples were placed on ice and processed using a Corning 165 gas-analyser within two hours of sampling. The values were corrected to body temperature using published charts.

Table 10.1(a): Clinical and sedation notes for Arabian Oryx sedated with etorphine and xylazine

Location	Sex	Age Years	Age Months	Weight (kg)	Anaesthetic/clinical details
OMAN (Sedated for radio collaring, all except one clinically normal)	M	2*		65*	High etorphine dose (4 mg) poor recovery (semi-narcotised 60-minute post antagonist)
	F	2	8*	56.5*	Two darts necessary. Initial dose inadequate (2 mg etorphine, 10 mg xylazine)
	M	2	6*	64*	Unremarkable
	F	2	8*	64.5*	Unremarkable
	F	2	2*	61.5*	2 mg etorphine, 15 mg xylazine, inadequate for sedation on two occasions. Sub-optimal condition prior to darting. Died after second darting and restraint
SAUDI (Sedated for treatment or translocation)	M	5		95	Fight wounds, lacerated hoof, laminitis and claw demormity
	M	5		100	Sedated twice. Fight wounds, necrosis of bulb of heel and sole. 3.8 mg etorphine, 30 mg xylazine, light sedation
	M	4		90	Fight wounds. Infection and gangrenous necrosis of hind leg. Sedated twice.
	M	3		70	Fight wounds. Osteomyelitis of metacarpus. 3.8 mg etorphine, 30 mg xylazine, deep sedation
	M	4		65	Cachexia. Pasteurella pneumonia, 3 mg etorphine, 20 mg xylazine, poor recovery, weak. Died two days later
	M	6		120	Dominant male, clinically normal
	F	5		100	Unremarkable
	F	4		85	Unremarkable
WHIPSNADE (Sedated on two occasions, all clinically normal)	(A) M	2*		75*	3 mg etorphine, 25 mg xylazine, excitable on darting, subordinate individual. Highest mean arterial pressure and rectal temperature
	(B) M	4*		90*	Excitable on darting
	(C) M	6*		103*	Dominant and excessively fat. No excitation on darting, lowest mean arterial pressure and rectal temperature noted during sedation (65 mmHg, 36.8°C). Some residual narcotisation 48 hours later

Note: * Known age and accurate body weights.

93

Chemical Immobilisation of Arabian Oryx

Table 10.1(b): Drugs, doses and sedation times in Arabian Oryx immobilised with etorphine and xylazine

	Confined Whipsnade	Unconfined Saudi Arabia	Oman
M99	0.034 ± 0.004	0.042 ± 0.005	0.037 ± 0.011
XYL	0.32 ± 0.02	0.33 ± 0.04	0.22 ± 0.04
ANIMALS DARTED	6	10	6(3)[a]
INDUCTION	4.7 ± 1.4	6.0 ± 2.0	2.27 ± 0.4
SEDATION	52 ± 22	40 ± 22	–
RECOVERY	6.0 ± 1.4	2.5 ± 0.5	2 ± 1

Note: a. Darting was unsuccessful on three occasions. Induction data based on three sedations.

General Notes: All doses mg/kg ± I.S.D.
Induction Time — Min: Period from darting to recumbency.
Sedation Time — Min: Period from darting until reversed.
Recovery Time — Min: Period from injection of antagonists until standing.
M 99 = etorphine (C-Vet Limited); XYL = xylazine (Rompun-Bayer).

Antagonists: In all cases a narcotic antagonist (diprenorphine 3 mg/ml) was administered intravenously in an equal volume to the etorphine (2.25 mg/ml dose. In Saudi Arabia and Whipsnade alpha-2 agonist antagonists—Idazoxan (15 mg) or RX821002A (1 mg) Reckitt & Coleman—were given in addition, to reverse the xylazine effect.

Results

Immobilisation using a combination of etorphine and xylazine was successful in 95% of the Oryx darted. Dosages above 0.04 mg/kg of etorphine and 0.3 mg/kg of xylazine were successful whatever the circumstances. The doses below this were unreliable in un-confined-range circumstances. Doses as low as 0.03 mg/kg of etorphine and 0.3 mg/kg of xylazine were satisfactory in animals acclimatised to confinement. Prolonged recovery was notable on three occasions, one of which was attributable to the severely debilitated condition of the subject. Another animal was considered to be excessively fat and showed prolonged narcotisation for two days after initial immobilisation. The third, which received a very much higher dose than the average, showed narcotisation for some time after sedation. In general, recovery was uncomplicated and animals which received the average dose returned to a normal state of activity within minutes.

Table 10.2: Mean respiration rates and rectal temperatures in confined Arabian Oryx during a 60-minute sedation with etorphine and xylazine

	Oryx	Initial	After 60 minutes
T °C	(A)	42	40
	(B)	40.2	39.8
	(C)	37.2	36.6
		Rate	Recordings (approx. 10-minute intervals)
Respiration rate (breaths per minute)	(A)	64 ± 24	8
	(B)	50 ± 20	5
	(C)	78 ± 11	6

Figure 10.1: Arabian Oryx heart rates and mean arterial pressures (*confined animals*: sedation: etorphine/xylazine)

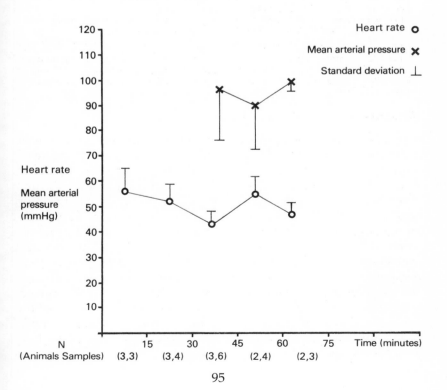

Figure 10.2: Arabian Oryx: blood gases (*confined animals*: sedation (etorphine/xylazine)

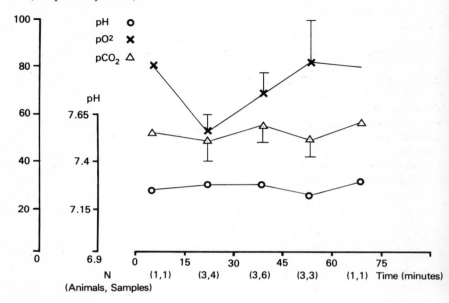

Figure 10.3: Electrocardiograph and systemic arterial pressure trace recorded for a male Arabian Oryx (C) 47 minutes after darting with etorphine (0.034 mg/kg) and xylazine (0.3 mg/kg)

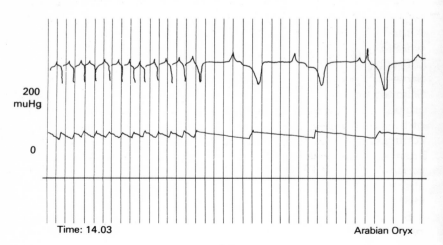

Physiological measurements undertaken in the Whipsnade group are recorded in Table 10.2 and Figures 10.1, 10.2 and 10.3. The animals were hypoxic and mildly hypercapnic (defined as a level pO^2 less than 80 millimetres Hg, pCO^2 greater than 43 millimetres Hg) (Lumb and Jones, 1984), with a high initial rectal temperature of 39.8 ± 2°C dropping by approximately 0.9 ± 0.8°C over 60 minutes of sedation. The pH of the blood remained within normal limits and relatively constant. Respiration was erratic, with a low tidal volume and polypnoea. There was some improvement in blood oxygen partial pressure (pO^2) with time, but carbon dioxide partial pressures (pCO_2) remained relatively constant. Mean arterial blood pressure was within acceptable physiological limits during the sedation, with the lowest pressure in a tamer, quieter individual (70 millimetres Hg). Heart rates remained relatively constant and no electrocardiographic abnormalities were detected.

In summary, the respiratory system was depressed, the cardio-vascular system was stable. The acid-base balance in the blood was maintained within normal limits. A reduction in rectal temperature was noted.

Discussion

Etorphine is a very potent derivative of morphine with analgesic, sedative and relaxant properties. Xylazine is a sedative agent with powerful analgesic and muscle-relaxant properties. Etorphine used alone in the family Bovidae (which includes a majority of the African antelopes) sometimes produces marked excitability during induction (Jones, 1972; Harthoorn, 1976). This was also noted in Arabian Oryx (Machado *et al.*, 1983). Xylazine can produce profound sedation in domestic bovines which resembles a deep narcosis (Hall and Clarke, 1983). The use of xylazine alone in wild or non-domesticated ungulates is unpredictable, and in many instances very high doses produce little or no sedative effect (Hime and Jones, 1970). The use of etorphine in combination with xylazine has been recommended, particularly in the large wild Bovidae, as early as 1972 (Jones, 1972) and there is evidence of synergism which reduced the dosage requirement of each component. The xylazine counteracts the excitation phase commonly seen with etorphine alone, and the time to recumbency after darting is also markedly reduced.

It is well recognised that there is a variable response to immobilising agents within a species and that this is associated not only with individual variation, but also with the circumstances in which the animals live. Wild or extensively managed non-domesticated ungulates demonstrate a marked flight response and excitability when darted; animals under confined conditions which are used to handling remain calmer when darted. The physiological response of an animal to stress of this kind is mediated through the autonomic nervous system. Narcotic and sedative combinations can have a marked effect on the physiology of ungulates and the interaction of these agents with the body's neuro-chemistry is complex (Kock and Pearce, 1985).

From the results, it is clear that unconfined, free-ranging animals require higher doses for satisfactory sedation than those under captive, confined conditions. Doses given in this paper are a guide to what has been effective under different conditions and what appears to be physiologically safe. While it is possible to overdose and produce undesirable side effects, it is considered that under-dosing, which can lead to marked excitation, may present a greater hazard. In a free-ranging animal, this can lead to muscular exhaustion, myopathies, hyperthermia and death. In the desert, excited, darted Arabian Oryx tend to run continuously until the absorbed drugs interfere with locomotion. The sooner an animal is immobilised in these circumstances the better. It was notable that, even under captive conditions, the Oryx quickly developed a high body temperature, but this may not be serious in this species. Ungulates adapted to desert and arid regions may possess thermo-regulatory control similar to the Camel *Camelus dromedarius*, which exhibits diurnal variation in body temperature (Higgins and Kock, 1986).

Dosage calculations of immobilising drugs should therefore take into consideration the relative tameness, environment and bodily condition (including the relative fatness) of the animal and the depth of sedation required for the proposed procedure. Of these variables, the authors consider that the degree of excitation is the most important consideration when calculating dosage. With the advent of alpha-2 agonist antagonists which will reverse the effects of xylazine, there is no need to use minimal doses of this agent. This is an advantage, as the dose of xylazine appears to be critical for smooth and rapid sedation, particularly under field conditions. The system of remote injection used should be compatible with the species. The Oryx possess thick skins, and needles of 1½ inches should be used whatever the injection system. Strong metal darts are ideal for field conditions.

The physiological response of the Arabian Oryx to sedation with etorphine and xylazine is comparable with that seen in the Scimitar-horned Oryx (Kock and Pearce, 1985). The polypnoea recorded is a notable difference (30–40 breaths per minute in Scimitar-horned Oryx) and is not entirely explained by any alteration in blood gases and acid-base balance. This may be a direct drug effect on the central nervous system due to hypoxia or possibly associated with the elevated body temperature. Whatever the cause, it is not associated with adverse physiology apart from hypoxia. Provision should be made for supplemental oxygen, especially when animals are debilitated or suffering respiratory insufficiency. While it is inadvisable to dart stressed animals, circumstances sometimes necessitate this action and high doses are necessary. The tamer the animal, the less the sympathetic response to the sedation procedure, and this is reflected in lower blood pressure and body temperature. In more excited animals, these parameters will tend to be elevated, but in general the cardiovascular and respiratory physiology can be expected to remain within safe limits.

Temperature loss is common in all species under anaesthesia, but perhaps more so in the desert oryx. Temperature regulation is likely to be complex in these species, as already discussed, and may explain the rapid temperature loss during sedation.

In order to reduce the risks of inhalation of regurgitated ruminal content or saliva, it is advisable to intubate the Oryx. This will also allow the provision of oxygen. In addition, where animals are not maintained in sternal recumbency, when bloat is a risk (particularly with higher doses of xylazine), a stomach tube should be inserted. Starvation prior to sedation although optimal is not necessary if these procedures are undertaken, and in any case is not a guarantee of preventing regurgitation.

The apparent persistent narcotisation of animals after administration of diprenorphine is, in the authors' opinion, more likely to be due to high doses of narcotic and is often associated with animals with large fat reserves. The drug etorphine is highly fat soluble and it is probable that the diprenorphine plasma concentration will decline more rapidly than the etorphine, leading to a return of the partially narcotised state. Since diprenorphine has some agonist action, it is unlikely that initially high reversal doses will reduce this problem.

The administration of an intramuscular dose of diprenorphine (in addition to the recommended intravenous dose) when reversing etorphine narcosis may help. Should partial narcosis return several hours after the initial sedation has been reversed, a further intramuscular dose of diprenorphine will usually result in complete recovery.

The alpha-2 agonist antagonists used in the sedation reported are not commercially available. Another anpha-2 agonist antagonist, yohimbine (Antagonil Wildlife Labs Inc.) is on sale in the United States, but its effect in Bovidae is variable. It is probable that one or other of the more specific antagonists will become commercially available in the near future.

The two deaths that occurred were both related to debility of animals in which any form of restraint was likely to result in death. The recovery of animals suffering from severe wounds and infections underlines the relative safety of this combination.

Conclusion

Etorphine with additional xylazine is a satisfactory sedative for immobilising confined or unconfined Arabian Oryx for procedures up to 60 minutes' duration. Normal anaesthetic protocol for ruminants must be adhered to. The use of specific reversing agents and correct dosages is essential for uncomplicated anaesthesia and recovery. Supplemental oxygen should be available if possible.

Acknowledgments

The authors would like to thank the following for the opportunity to undertake this work: The Food & Agricultural Organisation (United Nations); Office of the Adviser for Conservation of the Environment, Sultanate of Oman; the National Commission for Wildlife Conservation and Development (NCWCD), Saudi Arabia; Zoological Society of London. In particular we would like to thank the Diwan of Royal Court Affairs, Oman; Dr Abu Zinada of the NCWCD, Saudi Arabia; Richard Cinderey for technical assistance; Dena Hickman for typing the manuscript and Terry Dennett for photography.

References

Fowler, M.E. (1986) *Zoo and Wild Animal Medicine*. 2nd Ed. W.B. Saunders Co., London.

Haigh, J.C. (1976) The immobilisation of Bongo (*Boocercus eurycerus*) and other African antelopes in captivity. *Vet. Rec. 98*: 237–9.

Hall, L.W., and Clarke, K.W. (1983) *Veterinary Anaesthesia*. 8th Ed. Balliere and Tindall, London.

Harthoorn, A.M. (1976) *The Chemical Capture of Animals*. Bailliere and Tindall, London.

Higgins, A.J., and Kock, R.A. (1986) In Higgins, A. J. (ed.), *The Camel in Health and Disease*. Balliere and Tindall, London: pp. 21–41.

Hime, J.M., and Jones, D.M. (1970) The use of xylazine in captive wild animals. *Verhandlungs Bericht des XI Internationale Symposiums über die Erkrankungen der Zootiere, Budapest.* Akademie-Verlag, Berlin.

Jones, D.M. (1972) The use of drugs for immobilisation, capture and translocation of non-domestic anfimals. *Veterinary Annual 12*: 320–52.

Jones, D.M. (1977) Recent advances in the use of drugs for immobilisation, capture and translocation of non-domestic animals. *Veterinary Annual 17*: 280.

Jones, D.M. (1978) *Verhandlungs Bericht des XX Internatifonale Symposiums über die Erkrankungen der Zootiere.* Akademie-Verlag, Berlin.

Kock, R.A. (1988) Veterinary aspects of the Hippotraginae. (This volume.)

Kock, R.A., and Pearce, P.C. (1985) Anaesthesia in zoo ungulates. *J. Association Veterinary Anaesthetists 13*: 59–89.

Lumb, W.B., and Jones, E.W. (1984) *Textbook of Veterinary Anaesthesia*, 2nd Ed. Lea and Fibiger, Philadelphia.

Machado, C.R., Furley, C.W., and Hood, H. (1983) Observation on the use of M99, Immobilon and Xylazine in the Arabian Oryx (*Oryx leucoryx*). *J. Zoo An. Med. 14*: 107–10.

Pearce, P.C., Knight, J.A., Hulton, R.A., Pugsley, S.L., and Hawkey, C.M. (1985) Disseminated intravascular coagulation associated with inhalation pneumonitis in a Scimitar-horned oryx (*Oryx tao*). *Vet. Rec. 116*: 189–90.

Pearce, P.C., and Kock, R.A. (1987) In press.

Wallach, J.D., and Boever, W.J. (1983) *Diseases of Exotic Animals*. W.B. Saunders Co., London.

Wiesner, H., Rietschel, W., and Gatesman, T. (1982) Practical experiences with the combination of Immobilon and Rompun in zoo animals. *Kolner Zoo 25* (2): 47–55.

11. Social Organisation and Ranging Behaviour in the Hippotraginae

Timothy Wacher

The Hippotraginae antelopes, that is the five forms of oryx *Oryx* spp., Roan Antelope *Hippotragus equinus*, Sable Antelope *H. niger* and Addax *Addax nasomaculatus*, are all notable for their bold appearance. They possess dramatic horns, carried by males and females alike, and have colourful and strongly marked coat patterns. These facts alone suggest that accurate signalling of information about social status is likely to be of particular importance in this group. The five oryx, Arabian *Oryx leucoryx*, Scimitar-horned *O. dammah*, Beisa *O. gazella beisa*, Fringe-eared *O. g. calotis* and Gemsbok *O. g. gazella*, together with the Addax, are further distinguished by their capacity to thrive in harshly arid environments.

These features contribute to a subjective perception that these antelopes are especially distinguished. In the case of the Arabian Oryx, prestige attached to the successful slaying of such a manifestly competent and adept desert-dweller was one of the factors encouraging the excessive hunting pressure that led to the original extinction of this species in the wild.

The successful effort to prevent the total extinction of the Arabian Oryx has resulted in a large and unique body of information on the captive breeding and management of this species and on its re-introduction into the wild. The purpose of this chapter is to set one aspect of the studies on the Arabian Oryx, namely their developing social organisation and ranging pattern at Yalooni, in the deserts of Oman, within the wider context of comparative information from the species' close relatives in continental Africa. This approach is of particular interest, since it has become widely appreciated that social organisation and behaviour is intimately related to variation in environmental conditions, a point that is particularly well illustrated within the antelopes as a whole

(Jarman, 1974). To take a simple example, the spatial distribution of essential resources, say the seasonal pattern of food supply, can critically influence the number of animals that can be together at one place. Hence, by reviewing the observed behaviour of essentially rather similar animals, in this case the five forms of oryx, living over a range of environmental conditions, one might expect to see variation in social organisation that reflects habitat differences. This in turn can give insight into the mechanisms by which these impressive animals thrive in 'difficult' habitats, and into some of the constraints acting upon them.

No other Hippotraginae species has received sufficient attention to match the wealth of information now available for the Arabian Oryx. A considerable body of knowledge on the status of the Fringe-eared Oryx has, however, been accumulated on the Galana Ranch in southeast Kenya, where the species has attracted attention as a possible domesticant. Galana Ranch lies at the heart of the limited range of Fringe-eared Oryx in East Africa, and supports a good population of completely wild Oryx within its 6,000 km^2 of unfenced grasslands and woodlands. Whilst the Galana area is regarded as lying within the semi-arid zone, annual rainfall of 400–800 millimetres represents at least four times that encountered at Yalooni. The vegetation is correspondingly more abundant and productive, and Fringe-eared Oryx at Galana enjoy one of the 'richest' environments regularly inhabited by any of the five oryx types. It is not surprising, therefore, that the local population densities found at Galana are among the highest reported for oryx (1.4/km^2) over any extensive region.

Hence, I shall proceed by describing the broad features of the social organisation and ranging behaviour of Fringe-eared Oryx at Galana, which can be compared with the detailed description of Arabian Oryx in the chapter by Mark Stanley Price on Field Operations and Research in Oman. This contrasts the two species living at extremes of an environmental-richness gradient, at least with respect to the range of habitats naturally occupied by oryx. It will then be possible to consider oryx species living in the 'intermediate' areas (Scimitar-horned, Beisa and Gemsbok), to see how they relate to the first two, and to make a brief review of the other Hippotraginae.

It is, of course, highly artificial to rank the species as if each were placed discretely along an environmental-quality gradient in this way. It is apparent that each experiences a range of conditions, and

103

in real life there will be considerable overlap between species. In addition, the range of the gradient is narrow, all the habitats are arid or semi-arid, although this problem can be reduced by incorporating the Roan and Sable Antelopes, which inhabit wetter regions than any of the oryx. Nevertheless, in the first instance it is of interest to establish overall trends, and a degree of simplification is necessary and useful in achieving this.

Fringe-eared Oryx on Galana Ranch

The social organisation and ranging behaviour of Fringe-eared Oryx were studied at Galana Ranch by fitting wild individuals with radio-tagged collars (Wacher, 1986). This makes it possible to follow the fortunes of individuals and observe how group sizes and movements vary through full seasonal and reproductive cycles.

Movements and Group Structure

Female Fringe-eared Oryx, and some males (mostly but not exclusively sub-adult males), show a movement pattern similar in form to that found in the re-introduced Arabian Oryx herds in Oman, though with the difference that the movements were carried out on a very much smaller scale. No individuals were found to exceed total ranges of 400 km². Like Arabian Oryx, they tend to be resident in small areas for variable lengths of time, interspersed with sometimes quite sudden and discreet shifts to new locations within the overall range. These shifts were often associated with the onset of rainfall and the appearance of green vegetation.

Fringe-eared Oryx herds tend to vary in size from day to day and from season to season. Whilst the population shows a typical group size of 30–40 individuals, radio-collared individuals often experience daily change in group size, and in most cases a very wide range of group sizes overall. Large aggregations of several hundred animals may form in the wet season when fresh grazing is abundant.

Herds frequented by females and the herd-living males are usually of mixed sex composition among the adults (10–30% adult males). Herds of bachelor males are very seldom encountered; on the handful of occasions that they were seen at Galana, knowledge of the previous and subsequent behaviour of the known individuals involved established that these were very short-term associations.

Territorial Males

Some males show a quite distinct movement pattern in that they restrict themselves to 5–8 km^2 territories; a few of these were known to remain on the same territories for up to two or three years. They were the only members of the population observed using a squatting posture when defaecating, and this was typically done at one of numerous 'dung sites' (located on bare ground and used repeatedly) which are scattered throughout the territory. They also differ from the rest of the population in that they are more often than not found alone.

Excursions off the territory are relatively rare. One radio-collared territorial male made the day-long 20-kilometre round trip to drink from the Galana River at four- to five-day intervals in the height of the dry season, but ceased doing this at other times.

The solitary territorial males superficially present a paradox: why spend most of your life alone if the remaining males are in more or less constant association with the breeding-age females in mixed-sex herds? Part of the explanation lies with the breeding biology of the Oryx, and especially the behaviour of females when calving.

The Breeding System

Fringe-eared Oryx at Galana are normally able to maintain a nine-month calving interval. Thus, each healthy female will give birth after an 8½-month gestation and will usually become pregnant again within two to three weeks as a result of mating during post-partum oestrus. This is known primarily through the long-term monitoring of individual domestic female Oryx at Galana, but in a small number of wild females it was confirmed that they too maintain a similar high rate.

Close observation of radio-collared females in the days around calving confirms that they are likely to move aside from the herds and to calve alone. The newborn calf lies hidden for the first two or three weeks of life, so relies on crypsis to avoid detection, which may be an important reason for isolation behaviour by the female. It is at this very time that the mother is coming into post-partum oestrus. In the case of radio-collared females, it was found that they are then likely to form temporary consortships with single territorial males, in some cases moving between the territories of several different males. The mother and calf typically resume a herd-living existence three to four weeks after the birth.

Independent observations of radio-collared territorial males confirmed that, if not alone, they are most likely to be seen with single adult females. In a good proportion of cases, it could be confirmed that the females concerned were, or were likely to be, mothers of newborn calves. In these circumstances, territorial males often indulged in vigorous attempts to herd both the mother and her offspring should they threaten to cross the territory boundary; they were not always successful.

In summary, these observations indicate some important features of the social system of Fringe-eared Oryx at Galana. The nine-month calving cycle of the females means that births are not closely synchronised with any particular season and, indeed, newborn calves may be encountered at any time of the year. Because females usually conceive at post-partum oestrus, this also means that sexually receptive females are likewise to be found at all times of the year. The location of these females is not easily predictable, partly because of the movement pattern of Oryx herds and partly because of the need to isolate from the herds when giving birth.

These tendencies, which from an adult male's perspective might make receptive females difficult to locate, are probably countered to some extent by the high density of Oryx. Hence, by taking up residence in a suitable area, an individual male may expect to encounter females on a more or less regular basis. That this does occur has been confirmed by following the fortunes of individual territorial males.

Hence, under the conditions found at Galana, it is known that some males adopt a territorial strategy. It remains possible, even probable, that such territorial males are not able to control all the matings. The system described above is a general trend apparent from observations on a few individuals, but there is little reason to suppose that it is rigidly adhered to in every case. It is bound to happen that on occasion oestrus females will be found in herds; first-time breeders or females that missed post-partum oestrus as a result of poor condition at calving may be examples, and numerous other events that may interrupt the basic sequence can be envisaged. This would suggest the possibility that some males, unable to hold territories, may still be able to obtain mating opportunities. Nevertheless, the very existence of the territorial males, coupled with the regular observation that they were invariably dominant to intruding herd males (or intruding territorial neighbours), strongly supports the notion that there is a considerable advantage in being territorial for Fringe-eared Oryx males at Galana.

The phenomenon of territoriality is entirely absent in re-introduced Arabian Oryx, where individual dominant males stay with mobile herds of stable membership, mate with the females and show sophisticated behaviour in protecting the calf and controlling herd movements (Stanley Price, this volume, pp. 18–34). Since the movements of the Arabian Oryx are much greater in extent, and the absolute density of Arabian Oryx is very much lower, this kind of behaviour makes very good sense. What is more, in view of the low water availability and productivity of Arabian Oryx habitat, there is reason to suppose that Arabian Oryx populations were always highly mobile and of comparatively low density. Hence, whilst the current isolation of the re-introduced groups is extreme, rarity of encounters with other Oryx may be comparatively normal in this species and one might expect a premium on behaviours which serve to enhance group cohesion.

Other Oryx

There are few detailed studies of oryx in other areas which allow detailed assessment of the role and status of individuals in the population. Other accounts of Fringe-eared Oryx are confined to a few observations reported from the eastern Serengeti, at the extreme limit of the species' range (Walther, 1978). Groups here were noted to be of mixed-sex composition and the role of 'alpha-bulls' in controlling the movements of herds was apparent. Single bulls were also noted, however, as was the fact that dominant herd bulls 'can also leave a herd without complications'. A female with neonate calf was also seen to leave a herd and spend time alone. These observations show features compatible both with the system operated by Arabian Oryx and with the situation at Galana. The short time span of observations in this case prevents firm conclusions as to the true status of the individuals involved, but they nevertheless emphasise the potential subtlety in variation between herd-living and territorial status for male Oryx.

There is virtually no published information on the social behaviour of Beisa Oryx, an obvious area for future attention. More detailed information is available for the Gemsbok in southern Africa. It has been reported that, within a restricted (40-km^2) and fenced game reserve, some adult males retained 7-km^2 territories, whilst the remainder lived in mixed-sex groups (Dieckmann, 1980). Females of this population also carved at nine-month intervals and did not synchronise birth seasons. Although calves did lie out for three to six weeks post-partum, females did not invariably isolate at this time and specific consortships between females and territorial males were not identified as a feature. Accounts of post-partum behaviour by females, however, refer several times to their associating with territorial males.

A radio-tracking study of Gemsbok in the Kalahari National Park has shown that some males live in restricted areas along dry river beds and it is thought likely that they will turn out to be territorial (Knight, pers. comm.). Individual females cover much larger areas of the dune habitats away from the river beds, using ranges in excess of 400 km^2 (Knight, pers. comm.).

The Scimitar-horned Oryx of the Sahel has recently suffered a decline almost as catastrophic as that of the Arabian Oryx (Newby, this volume, pp. 159–60). In this species again, information about its normal social system is sparse, not least because of the remote, harsh habitats it favours and, more recently, its extreme rarity. It is known, however, that Scimitar-horned Oryx are highly nomadic, individuals probably covering very large areas, and that they live in groups of variable size; aggregations of several hundred animals were once not unusual in suitable areas following rainfall. Detailed observations of calving and reproductive behaviour are few, but there are intriguing references to small groups of pregnant females being seen in the company of males and even of 'old' males being seen entirely alone or in the company of Dama Gazelles *Gazella dama*. (Territorial Fringe-eared Oryx frequently keep company with other species, notably Peters' Gazelle *Gazella granti petersi*, on Galana.)

Again, it is not possible from available information to draw firm conclusions, but Scimitar-horned Oryx clearly share with Arabian Oryx the capacity to roam over very large areas. It is of great interest to resolve the status of the reported single males, though unfortunately it may no longer be possible to do this in the natural wild populations. There remains a fascinating opportunity to investigate this kind of problem in schemes such as the Scimitar-horned Oryx re-introduction project currently being carried out at Bou-Hedma in Tunisia (Bertram, this volume, pp. 136–145).

Addax, Roan and Sable

The remaining Hippotraginae are taxonomically more distinct from the oryx group, but the Roan and Sable Antelopes in particular are valuable for providing examples of Hippotraginae social organisation in generally moister habitats than those favoured by oryx.

Very little is known about social behaviour in wild Addax populations, for almost parallel reasons to the situation in Scimitar-horned Oryx. This species has also been noted for a capacity to move over large areas, and large aggregations used to occur in wet seasons. Group sizes in recent times are usually fairly small and of mixed-sex composition, though solitary males may be encountered.

Sable Antelope have been studied at various locations in southern and East Africa, although in some cases the study populations have been restricted to small areas. In the lower-rainfall parts of its range in southern Africa it is thought likely that Sable Antelope herds move over ranges of 200–300 km^2 (Estes, 1974). It is usually noted that herds are composed of adult females with young and a proportion of sub-adult males, but that usually only one black-coated fully adult male is present. Detailed study of social structure in study populations, such as that at Shimba Hills in Kenya, has shown that black-coated males are territorial. Shimba Hills has special interest in the current case, because its proximity to the coast in southern Kenya ensures that it has abundant rainfall of 1,000 millimetres per year or more. It is a small area, vegetated with a rich mosaic of tall forest and open meadow. Under these conditions, Sable Antelope live at a high local density in permanent herds of fixed membership. Each herd has a discrete range, overlapping the territories of three or four adult males. Whilst herds are of closed membership, it has been noted that each herd may split into temporary sub-units from time to time, and that these splits do not appear to occur in the same way on each occasion.

The range of the Roan Antelope, through West and Central Africa right down into southern Africa, is significantly larger than that of any other Hippotraginae, so this is potentially a particularly valuable species for a comparative approach of this kind. It is unfortunate, therefore, that information on its social system is available from only one part of its range in South Africa. Here it is reported that Roan Antelope live in small 'harem' groups of

109

females and young, associated with a single dominant male who is intolerant of other males. These harem groups live within 60–100-km² exclusive ranges (Joubert, 1974).

Discussion

The comparison of Hippotraginae social systems over a range of habitats has revealed a number of differences between species. Among the most striking are the very large differences in range sizes, in which it is apparent that those species living in the driest areas make the most extensive movements, and the existence of territoriality among males in some cases but not others.

These observations strongly suggest that oryx as a genus exhibit different social organisations in different regions. Territoriality is probably a successful mating strategy for Fringe-eared Oryx in the high-density populations of the southern areas of Galana Ranch and it appears to be in operation in the studied populations of Gemsbok. In both these populations, other males live in mixed-sex herds, where they may exhibit herding behaviour and attempt to control herd movement. Hence, the existence of territorial males, and their known role in courtship behaviour at Galana, shows that under some conditions there is an advantage in territoriality. It remains possible that these males do not monopolise all mating opportunities, and it is possible to postulate a two-strategy system with a balance between the proportion of territorial to non-territorial herd males.

At Galana, territorial males were prominent in the population, but in the Serengeti this was not so and this may be related to the fact that this is a small population at the edge of the species' range. The absence of territoriality in the Arabian Oryx makes very good sense, as has been discussed; a territorial male under these conditions could not expect to encounter very many receptive females.

I have summarised a preliminary scheme which makes a first step towards unifying these different organisation patterns within the Hippotraginae in Figure 11.1, which plots range size for males and females separately against mean annual rainfall in the study areas for which data are available. The negative relationship between female range size and mean rainfall pattern is expected, given the known relationship between rainfall and primary production in the vegetation (Rosenzweig, 1968; Coe et al., 1976) and

Figure 11.1: Schematic representation relating ranging behaviour of male and female Hippotraginae species to mean annual rainfall

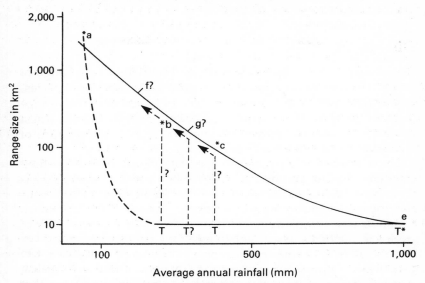

Note: It would be more accurate to represent each species as occupying a cloud of points, which in some cases might be large. The five data points shown (*) are selected to show the known extremes: specific references are given in the key below.

(a)   Arabian Oryx at Yalooni, Oman (Stanley Price, 1986).
(b)   Gemsbok in the Kalahari (Knight, pers. comm.).
(c)   Fringe-eared Oryx at Galana (Wacher, 1986).
(d)   Roan Antelope in Kruger National Park (Joubert, 1974).
(e)   Sable Antelope at Shimba Hills, Kenya (Estes, 1974). NB: This species probably uses much larger areas in most of its range, where the status of males is less certain.
(f)   Possible typical location of Scimitar-horned Oryx?
(g)   Possible typical location of Beisa Oryx?

NB: Short-dashed lines join territories of males (T) to female range sizes, and imply that the occurrence of territorial males may be expected to drop out as one moves down the rainfall gradient.

the relationship between range size and energy requirements (Mace *et al.*, 1984).

This schematic representation assumes the established fact that reproducing females are more sensitive to aspects of food supply than adult males on account of the greater nutritional stresses incurred by gestation and lactation. The figure implies that, as one moves down the rainfall gradient, male Oryx species may be

111

expected to switch from a territorial to a herd-living strategy, mediated by the effect of low primary productivity on female dispersion patterns. Hence, it may be useful as a next step to add a third dimension, perhaps population density, that will model the effect of encounter rate between territorial males and receptive females. In this way, it may become possible to define a 'domain' within which the density and dispersion of females is adequate to make territoriality 'pay' in terms of reproductive success for males. Thus, one can think of the observed behaviour of females being influenced primarily by food dispersion; the behaviour of males is in turn governed by the distribution of females, particularly sexually receptive females.

Such a scheme further implies that social systems may be expected to vary within a species from place to place, if local conditions are sufficiently variable. It may be possible to account for observations of solitary Scimitar-horned Oryx males, for example, by postulating that they are adopting temporary territories in regions of localised aggregation. That social organisation is not a fixed attribute of a given species is already a well-established feature of some other antelope groups, the highly variable range of systems reported for the Topi being a case in point (Duncan, 1971; Jewell, 1972).

In summary, then, the Hippotraginae as a group reveal a range of social systems. It has been suggested that female response to food dispersion and male response to female dispersion are two key factors in this, and the available observations are consistent with this idea. Hence, for the Hippotraginae there appears to be a possibility of predicting the outline of a social system if consideration is given to the basics of rainfall and local primary productivity, and the known or expected population density. The framework is in need of considerable substantiation and refinement before it can claim any practical value, but further research on species such as the wide-ranging Roan Antelope and Beisa Oryx, both hitherto somewhat neglected, offers the chance to gain useful knowledge and at the same time test the rigour of the concepts used here.

References

Bertram, B.C.R. (1988) Re-introducing Scimitar-horned Oryx to Tunisia. (This volume.)

Coe, M.J., Cumming, D.H., and Philipson, J. (1976) Biomass and produc-

1. Wild Arabian Oryx *Oryx leucoryx* moving to new grazing in Oman (Photo courtesy of M. Stanley Price).

2. (a) Oryx with calf in Oman (Photo courtesy of M. Stanley Price).

(b) Released Oryx under shade at Yalooni (Photo courtesy of M. Stanley Price).

3. (a) Harasis rangers watch over an Oryx herd (Photo courtesy of M. Stanley Price).

(b) A ranger patrol in Oman (Photo courtesy of M. Stanley Price).

4. Scimitar-horned Oryx *Oryx dammah* at Bou-Hedma National Park, Tunisia (Photo courtesy of B.C.R. Bertram).

5. (a) Deep well surrounded by over-grazed desertified land, a typical
example of habitat degradation in the Sahel (Photo courtesy of J. Newby).

(b) A dying Scimitar-horned Oryx suffering from drought and exhaustion
(Photo courtesy of J.E. Newby)

6. (a) *Gazella dama ruficollis*, the desert form, at Marwell Zoo (Photo courtesy of Marwell Zoological Park).

   (b) *Gazella d. permista* from the Sudanese/Chad border (Photo courtesy of D.M. Jones).

Note the distinct colour variations between the subspecies. A third subspecies, from western Africa, is also dark.

7. *Gazella subgutturosa marica* in HM The Sultan of Oman's collection (Photo courtesy of D.M. Jones).

8.

(a) *Gazella gazella cora* at Yalooni in Oman (Photo courtesy of D.M. Jones).

(b) *Gazella dorcas* sub-adult male (Photo courtesy of D.M. Jones).

tion of large African herbivores in relation to rainfall and primary production. *Oecologia 22*: 314–54.

Dieckmann, R.C. (1980) The Ecology and Breeding Biology of the Gemsbok, *Oryx gazella gazella* (Linn. 1758), in the Hester Malan Nature Reserve, Unpubl. MSc thesis, University of Pretoria.

Duncan, P. (1971) Quoted in Jarman, P.J., and Jarman, M.V. (1979), The dynamics of ungulate social organisation. In Sinclair, A.R.E., and Norton-Griffiths, M. (eds.), *Serengeti: Dynamics of an Ecosystem*. University of Chicago Press, Chicago: pp. 185–220.

Estes, D. (1974) Social organisation of the African bovidae. In Geist, V., and Walther, F.R. (eds.), *The Behaviour of Ungulates and its Relation to Management*. IUCN Publ. No. 24, Vol. 1: 166–205.

Jarman, P.J. (1974) The social organisation of antelope in relation to their ecology. *Behaviour 48*: 215–67.

Jewell, P.A. (1972) Social organisation and movements of Topi (*Damaliscus korrigum*) during the rut at Ishasha, Q.E. National Park, Uganda. *Zoologica Africana 7*: 233–55.

Joubert, S.C.J. (1974) The social organisation of Roan Antelope, *Hippotragus equinus*, and its influence on the spatial distribution of herds in the Kruger National Park. In Geist, V., and Walther, F.R. (eds.), *The Behaviour of Ungulates and its Relation to Management*. IUCN Publ. No. 24, Vol. 2: 661–75.

Mace, G.M., Harvey, P.J., and Clutton-Brock, T.H. (1984) Vertebrate home range size and energetic requirement. In Swingland, I.R., and Greenwood, P.J. (eds.), *The Ecology of Animal Movement*. The Thetford Press, Thetford: pp. 35–53.

Rosenzweig, M.L. (1968) Net primary productivity of terrestrial communities: Prediction from climatological data. *American Naturalist 102*: 67–74.

Stanley Price, M.R. (1986) The re-introduction of Arabian Oryx *Oryx leucoryx* into Oman. *Int. Zoo Ybk 24/25*: 179–88.

Wacher, T.J. (1986) The Ecology and Social Organisation of Fringe-eared Oryx on the Galana Ranch, Kenya. Unpubl. D. Phil thesis, University of Oxford.

Walther, F.R. (1978) Behavioural observations of Oryx Antelope, (*Oryx beisa*), invading Serengeti National Park, Tanzania. *J. Mamm. 59*: 243–60.

12. Habitat Use and Ranging Behaviour of Kalahari Gemsbok (*Oryx gazella* Linnaeus, 1758)

Douglas Williamson and Jane Williamson

Rainfall in our northern Central Kalahari Game Reserve (CKGR) study area averages about 350 millimetres per year, but it is erratic in time and space, and surface water is often available for only a few months or weeks of the year. Since animals cannot live without water, finding moisture is a problem all residents of the area must solve. A further environmental stress to which resident animals are subjected is periods of very high temperature.

On the assumption that these factors, together with requirements for food and predator avoidance, would strongly influence Gemsbok *Oryx gazella gazella* habitat use, we assessed the various habitat types in our study area in terms of their ability to provide food, moisture and shade and to facilitate predator detection and avoidance. We found that it was reasonable to divide the complex mosaic of habitat types into just two categories, based on the clay content of the soil.

On the one hand, there is what we refer to as the pan and valley habitat, which has clay-rich soil (up to 60% clay), often with a calcrete hardpan about 30 centimetres below the surface. Pans are flat depressions in the landscape, from a few hectares to tens of square kilometres in area. Valleys are meandering, flat depressions up to 1–2 kilometres in width and up to hundreds of kilometres in length. Open, short grassland is the predominant vegetation type of this habitat. The standing crop of grass on pans and valleys may dwindle to close to zero by the end of the dry season. Clumps of trees do occur, as do occasional extensive stands of woody shrubs. Numerous depressions on pans and valleys hold water after rains, for periods of days, weeks or months, depending on the amount and frequency of rain. Absence of extensive tree cover means that shade is not abundant but that visibility is good so that predator detection and avoidance are facilitated.

On the other hand, there are what may be collectively described as the sandveld habitat types, on sandy soils with a minimal or non-existent clay fraction. The vegetation of these habitats ranges from open shrub and grassland plains to dunes with closed canopy woodland. Rain-filled waterholes are less common in these habitats than they are on pans and valleys, but they support an abundance of browse species, whose leaves contain up to 50% moisture during the height of the dry season and are heavily browsed by species such as Springbok *Antidorcas marsupialis* Zimmerman, 1780. Also common in the sandveld, but entirely absent from pans and valleys, are numerous plant species with underground storage organs with a moisture content of up to 70%, which are heavily utilised by Gemsbok (Williamson, 1987). Grass cover tends to be taller and more rank than that on pans and valleys, the maximum standing crop being four times higher than on pans and valleys (2,000 as against 500 kilograms dry matter per hectare). The higher density of woody plants in this habitat means that shade is generally more available than on pans and valleys, but that predator avoidance is presumably more problematic.

We documented patterns of Gemsbok habitat use by making repeated aerial surveys of a series of pans and valleys about 250 kilometres in length and by regional aerial surveys of all habitat types in an area of about 12,000 km^2. Both types of survey showed the same marked seasonal pattern of Gemsbok habitat use: concentration on pans and valleys after rainfall, and scattering into sandveld areas during dry periods. This is precisely the opposite to what happens in areas where permanent surface water is available. Thus, for example, along the Chobe River in northern Botswana, animals concentrate along the river during the dry season and scatter widely into the dryland areas during the rains.

A statistical analysis of the results from the pan and valleys surveys showed a high correlation (r=0.84, p<0.001) between the number of Gemsbok seen in this habitat and rainfall over the previous 21 days, soil moisture and the moisture content of the grass. Our data on environmental variables were collected from only a small segment of the survey route, and it is likely that more representative data would have produced an even higher correlation coefficient. From this analysis we inferred that rainfall is the principle factor influencing Gemsbok habitat use. This inference was confirmed by a further analysis which showed a similarly high correlation (r=0.82, p<0.001) between the number of Gemsbok on pans and valleys and rainfall alone (in this case, over the previous 30 days).

Statistical analysis of the regional survey results further confirmed the influence of rainfall on habitat use. These surveys were done less often than the pan and valley surveys, and we used effective rainfall (Stanley Price, 1977) rather than actual rainfall for this analysis because we believed that it more accurately reflected conditions for plant growth. Although pan and valley habitat accounted for only about 3% of the area surveyed, animals were more visible on pans and valleys than in other habitats and there was a high correlation ($r=0.89$, $p < 0.001$) between the total number of animals seen on regional surveys and the proportion seen on pans and valleys, i.e. the higher the proportion seen on pans and valleys, the higher the total number seen. Because of this, and because the use of just two categories of habitat meant that if animals were not in the one they were in the other, we used the proportion of Gemsbok seen on pans and valleys on each survey as an index of habitat use. We found a high correlation ($r=0.88$, $p < 0.001$) between this index and effective rainfall since the previous survey.

On the basis of these results, it seems plausible to suggest that rainfall is the primary influence on patterns of Gemsbok habitat use in the northern CKGR. We recognise that this analysis is based on important simplifying assumptions, but we believe that it is nevertheless valid.

We can offer no definitive explanation of why Gemsbok move onto pans and valleys after rainfall, but the factors mentioned earlier are almost certainly important. Immediately after rain, drinking water becomes available in the numerous waterholes on pans and valleys. This may attract Gemsbok. Within a few weeks of rain, new grass growth becomes available and may induce Gemsbok to remain on pans and valleys, although this effect may vary through time.

Our entire 3½-year study was undertaken during a period of below-average rainfall and we noticed that Gemsbok fed much less on pans and valleys than did Springbok. We suspect that the explanation for this is that the smaller bite size of the Springbok enables them to harvest shorter grass, and we infer that during periods of higher rainfall Gemsbok would feed more on pans and valleys. This inference was confirmed by San hunter-gatherer informants and by Mark and Delia Owens (pers. comm), who worked in our study area during a period of high rainfall. The relevance of this issue is that it suggests a need to be aware of climatic cycles with a period of more than one year. In southern Africa, there is evidence (Tyson and Dyer, 1978) for a 20-year cycle, encompassing a wetter decade, followed by a drier decade (or vice versa, depending on the starting point).

Our evidence that the openness of pans and valleys facilitates predator avoidance is purely anecdotal. We observed Gemsbok moving out of woodland onto a valley immediately after hearing Lion roars in the nearby woodland. San hunter-gatherer informants reported having made similar observations.

If the reasons why Gemsbok move onto pans and valleys after rain are not entirely clear, the reasons why they move into the sandveld during the dry season are very plain. By the end of the dry season, pans and valleys are distinctly inhospitable: they offer little grazing, little shade when temperatures in the shade often approach 50°C, and no source of moisture. At the same time, the sandveld offers an abundance of grazing and browse, abundant shade and a prolific supply of plant underground-storage organs.

Our observations of Gemsbok habitat use at the population level were augmented by the tracking of eight individual radio-collared animals, two females and six males, and repeated sightings of individually recognisable animals. Radio-collared Gemsbok were tracked for periods ranging from 18 to 39 months. Individually recognisable animals were known for periods ranging from three months to three years.

Radio-tracking was done almost entirely from the air and revealed a striking difference in the annual ranges of females and males. Female annual ranges varied from 52 to 212 km^2. Five of the males had annual ranges of between 10 and 16 km^2; the other male was a distinctly older animal and its annual ranges were 86 km^2 and 66 km^2 in two consecutive years. The probable explanation for the difference in the size of female and male annual ranges is that males with small ranges were territorial, while the older male has ceased to be so.

There was an indication that female range sizes were also influenced by age. One of the females was a yearling when collared and her ranges over the next three years were 212, 191 and 109 km^2. The other female was an adult when collared and her annual ranges over two years were 52 and 65 km^2. It may be significant that the young female produced a calf in the third year, when her range decreased to about half of what it was in the preceding two years.

The largest distance that a collared animal was observed to move over a 24-hour period was about 10 kilometres. Usually the distance moved in a 24-hour period was 1–2 kilometres, and often it was less than 1 kilometre.

Animals with larger ranges regularly returned to the same places, remaining within a radius of less than 1 kilometre for three to ten weeks at a time. Ground inspection of some of these places gave the impression that they were in areas where range conditions were exceptionally good because of high localised rainfall. Observations of individually recognisable animals also revealed a tendency to remain in such places for considerable periods of time.

Throughout our study we were struck by the apparent ease with which Gemsbok coped with the protracted drought in the Kalahari. Nearly all the animals we saw were in good condition and at all times we saw females with small offspring. This was during a period when a catastrophic die-off of Kalahari Wildebeest *Connochaetes taurinus* occurred and when livestock with access to borehole water were in very poor condition because the areas surrounding boreholes had been stripped of vegetation. We attributed the success of the Gemsbok in coping with the drought to their independence of surface water, which seems to be due largely to their ability to exploit underground plant storage organs as a source of moisture.

Acknowledgements

Permission to work in the CKGR was given by the Office of the President and the Department of Wildlife and National Parks, Botswana. Our research was funded by the Frankfurt Zoological Society and written up at Cambridge University at the invitation of Professor P.A. Jewell.

References

Stanley Price, M.R. (1977) The estimation of food intake and its seasonal variation in hartebeest. *E. Afr. Wildl. J. 15*: 33–49.

Tyson, P.D., and Dyer, T.G.J. (1978) The predicted above normal rainfall of the seventies and the likelihood of droughts in the eighties. *South African Journal of Science 74*: 372–7.

Williamson, D.T. (1987) Plant underground storage organs as a source of moisture for Kalahari wildlife. *African Journal of Ecology 23*: 63–4.

13. Scimitar-horned Oryx (*Oryx Dammah*) at Edinburgh Zoo

J.Paul Gill and Ann Cave-Browne

Introduction

The British herd of Scimitar-horned Oryx *Oryx dammah* is descended from 6:10 animals imported from Aalborg Zoo, Denmark, which arrived at Marwell Zoo in November 1971. Although some were wild-caught, it is not known how closely related the founder population was. These animals were followed in June 1972 by a pair from Hannover and a further male was imported from Paris in July 1982. The breeding programme throughout the UK is now co-ordinated by the regional studbook-keeper at the Zoological Society of London. This paper describes the management and behaviour, particularly vocalisations, of the Edinburgh herd of Scimitar-horned Oryx and includes a comparison of interspecific time budgets and habitat preferences as reflected in the use of the enclosure. Interspecific associations involving the Oryx and either the herd of Grant's Zebra *Equus burchellii* or the bachelor herd of crossed Red and Kafue Lechwe *Kobus leche leche* x *K. l. kafuensis* are also discussed.

Methodology

Detailed observations were made from 3 January to 14 February 1983 and between 4 July and 29 August 1985. A separate study of the vocalisations of the Oryx was undertaken from February to September 1984. At other times, behavioural observations and measurements have been recorded on an *ad hoc* basis outside the study period.

During the winter study, observations wre made for 2½ hours between 09.00 and 13.00 hours over 20 days. The summer study was carried out on eight days for two hours each day between 10.00 and 14.30 hours. The enclosure was divided into quadrants and the position and behaviour of each individual was recorded every ten minutes.

Interspecific interactions were noted for ten-minute periods and the animals were subjected to analysis of their behaviour when they were (i) standing and lying, (ii) moving and (iii) grazing. The distribution of each of these activities for each species within the paddock was entered onto duplicate maps, facilitating comparison between species. Results for summer activities are not directly comparable with the winter results since some adjustments for higher scores in certain quadrants were made.

Vocalisations were recorded using a battery-operated Aiwa S30 cassette recorder with a flat frequency response of 70 to 12,500 hertz and a hand-held Aiwa CM30 omnidirectional condenser microphone. Since the frequency response of the equipment was flat about 150 hertz, only loud calls were subseqently analysed. Between February and September 1984, over 24 hours of material was recorded which included more than 1,000 calls. As each vocalisation was recorded, the caller was identified, the loudness of the call estimated and the accompanying behaviour noted.

Seventy-one calls were analysed with a Kay 7800B digital sonagraph. Sounds had been selected from a wide range of contexts and were classified into various types of call. Parameters measured included duration, fundamental frequency and the frequencies of the first (F1), second (F2) and third (F3) formants.

Vocalisations are produced by vibrations of the vocal fold, which is part of the larynx. The fundamental frequency, or the rate of vocal-fold vibration, contributes only indirectly to the identity of a call. Formants, produced by resonances of a collection of harmonic vibrations within the vocal tract, are responsible for the distinctiveness of a call.

Animals

Full details of the animals are given in Table 13.1. The herd of Scimitar-horned Oryx at Edinburgh was founded with the arrival of three males in July 1981 and five females all from the Marwell herd. All animals were yearlings on arrival at Edinburgh, and the first calf was born in August 1983. An additional male, M 078, arrived in 1986. Up until 1987, 7:8 calves have been born, of which 6:6 have survived. Three calves born in 1985 formed part of the group re-introduced to Tunisia. On arrival, these calves, F G10, M G11 and M R12, were numbered 6, 7 and 8 respectively (Wacher,

Table 13.1: History of breeding Scimitar-horned Oryx at Edinburgh Zoo

ISIS No.	Tag No.	Sire	Dam	Date of Birth	Place of Birth	Arrived Edin. Zoo	Departed Edin. Zoo	Fate
810722	M 2	NE 115	NE 130	18.7.80	Marwell	8.7.81	14.2.84	Whipsnade
810723	M 3	NE 115	NE	2.7.80	Marwell	19.9.84	15.2.96	Culled
820425	F54	NE 100	NE183	25.6.81	Marwell	22.4.82		
820423	F 56	NE 100	NE 110	6.7.81	Marwell	22.4.82		
820424	F 57	NE 100	NE 112	7.7.81	Marwell	22.4.82		
820420	F 59	NE 100	NE	22.7.81	Marwell	22.4.82		
830807	F A	M 2	F 56	9.8.83	Edinburgh	9.8.83		
840205	M 4	M 2	F 57	25.2.84	Edinburgh	25.2.84	11.11.85	Private collection
840303	F 05	M 2	F 54	22.3.84	Edinburgh	22.3.84		
–	F R4	M 2	F 59	6.4.84	Edinburgh	6.4.84	14.4.84	Died
840504	F D	M 2	F 56	23.5.84	Edinburgh	23.5.84		
840501	F G10	M 3	F 54	19.5.85	Edinburgh	19.5.85	11.11.85	Tunisia
850502	F Black	M 3	F 57	23.5.85	Edinburgh	23.5.85	11.11.85	Marwell
850503	M G11	M 3	F 56	29.5.85	Edinburgh	29.5.85	11.11.85	Tunisia
850601	M R12	M 3	F 59	15.6.85	Edinburgh	15.6.85	11.11.85	Tunisia
860513	F Y11	M 3	F 57	31.5.86	Edinburgh	27.5.86		
860604	M R13	M 3	F 54	5.6.86	Edinburgh	5.6.86	20.5.87	Manor House
860605	M G7	M 3	F A	8.6.86	Edinburgh	8.6.86	20.5.87	Culled
860606	M B13	M 3	F 59	11.6.86	Edinburgh	11.6.86	20.5.87	Manor House
860804	M 02	M 3	F D	13.8.86	Edinburgh	13.8.86	6.9.86	Died
860513	M 078	197 M62	10 8F5	17.6.84	Marwell	31.10.86		

Note: M = male. F = Female.

1986a; Bertram, this volume, pp. 136–145. For the purposes of this study, calves were considered to become juveniles at one year and adults at two years.

Facilities

The African Plains exhibit at Edinburgh Zoo consists of a 2.6-hectare grass paddock with trees and associated pens and housing for the three species. Over-grazing has historically led to the spread of ragwort *Senecio jacobea*, nettles *Urtica* spp. and thistles *Cardus* spp. which, together with the areas of exposed rock, make parts of the enclosure unsuitable for grazing. Public viewing is from a raised wall to the west or through an 8-foot chainlink fence that surrounds all but the southern edge of the enclosure. Along with the mature trees and hillocks, the wall provides some shelter from the bitter westerly winds. The size of the paddock necessitates supplemental feeds which, along with the practice of night housing, interrupts the animals' natural activity cycle (O'Connor, 1986). The shape and varied terrain of the enclosure, however, favours normal activities during the day, especially with species such as Oryx and Zebra which are subject to disturbance from the public.

The oryx housing consists of one large house and pen with two adjoining loose boxes and smaller outside pens. Partly surfaced with well-drained shale, the remainder is concrete, ridged where appropriate to provide adequate grip. One of the large house gates and all the pen gates can be slid shut from some distance to separate animals. Lighting and electric sockets are provided.

Husbandry

The management regime at Edinburgh is based upon captive husbandry of the species at Marwell, London and Whipsnade Park Zoos, and maintains the same high standards of general welfare and breeding. The herd individuals are shut in their pens each evening and put into the paddock each morning. This occurs throughout the year except in the most severe weather and during the calving period, when the entire herd is kept inside. Because of the herd's familiarity with being shut in, stress is minimised on those occasions when they have to be confined. Until they learn the routine, the calves are walked into the Oryx housing, where they lie out on the bedding provided. When the male is present, he is separated at night into a small pen and loose box to prevent aggression towards the females and calves, which are held together.

In the late afternoon, each of the three species is fed supplemental food in their separate pens, thus avoiding interspecific competition. The problem of dominant individuals displacing conspecific subordinates from the food troughs is minimised by the provision of several troughs. The diet consists of dairy pellets (B), crushed oats and flaked maize in the ratio 20:5:2 by weight, and a handful of vitamin E pellets (C). The dietary requirements of vitamin E, copper and selenium (Jones, 1985) are met in the provided pellets. Mineralised salt licks are supplied. The addition of hydroponically grown and hand-pulled grass with lettuce may have contributed to the high survival rate of 1984 winter-born calves.

The following parasites have been isolated from the herd at various stages: *Camelostrongylus mentulatus*, *Nematodirus spathiger*, *N. helvetianus*, *Trichostrongylus colubriformis*, *Capillaria* spp., *Trichuris* spp. (Flach, 1986), *Dermatophilus congolense*, an as yet unidentified tapeworm and antibodies against Wildebeest *Connochaetes* spp. herpes virus.

Males cover females for two successive years before they are replaced. This reduces the possibility of most sire-daughter matings and helps equalise founder representation and family sizes. At Edinburgh, a single male is introduced to the female herd in September or October. Normally he serves all fertile females. Although calves may be born at any time of year, the removal of the male before calving starts ensures that the majority of births occur between May and September. In 1984, calves were born in winter because in the first year breeding was not controlled. In spite of evidence that winter-born calves suffer a significantly higher mortality, however, survival was good.

On the second day post-partum, while separated from the dam in one of the loose boxes, calves are examined, sexed, ear-tagged and given 20 millilitres of Grovax serovaccine (A) subcutaneously. Usually, calves and their dams are returned to the herd a few days after birth. Each animal is individually recognisable from large brightly coloured ear-tags which are correlated with the adults' distinctive face patterns and horn shape. Detailed records are maintained at Edinburgh and are submitted to the regional studbook-keeper and the International Species Inventory System (ISIS). Emphasis is placed upon keepers' understanding of the relationship between their records and wider management issues.

Results

Reproductive Behaviour

Oestrus females display pink and swollen vulvas, eat less, vocalise more, and solicit physical contact from the bull and other cows. Before the male was introduced in 1985 and 1986, there were so many attempts at mating by females that it was sometimes difficult to determine which was in oestrus. Copulations have been observed on several occasions. Courtship typically involves tight circling, with the male raising his foreleg close to the female's hindlegs (*laufslag*). During successful mounts, the female remains still, allowing the male to clasp her back with his forefeet and achieve full intromission. Since such behaviour is normally observed on only one day, peak oestrus probably lasts less than 24 hours.

Calculation of gestation periods for 12 pregnancies shows a range of 222 days to 253 days and a median of 249 days. The time lapse between F 56's first and second offspring, F A and F D, was 287 days (see Table 13.1). No other females have been served during their post-partum oestrus.

From the total of 7:8 births occurring before 1987, 4:4 took place between 08.00 and 17.00 hours. Signs of imminent parturition included a splayed-hindleg gait and general restlessness. A continuous record was made of the behaviour of a multiparous dam during parturition occurring in the midst of the herd. The foetal membranes and first hoof became visible 20 minutes before parturition. From this time, contractions occurred every two seconds as the dam alternately stood and sat down. While recumbent, the dam passed faeces twice before the head appeared and five minutes later she stood up, dropping the calf to the ground. She immediately ate the membranes as the neonate struggled to free itself. The dam's intense licking of the calf was interrupted only to allow her to drink the birth fluids lying on the ground. The calf made five attempts to stand, before succeeding after 20 minutes. This particular calf suckled 80 minutes after parturition, though others have taken over two hours. All Edinburgh-born Oryx showed an interest in the calf. An alarming complication occurred after 143 minutes, as the dam kicked her calf 15 times, apparently increasingly excited by the calf's calling. The placenta was passed 168 minutes after parturition and was later eaten.

Two calves weighed 10 kilos on the second day post-partum. Until the sixth week, the nose of a calf has a characteristic 'snub' appearance. Around the eighth week, the uniform beige calf coloration develops into the distinctive brown and cream adult pelage. Body weight and horn length increase rapidly, but adult size is not normally reached until after the second year.

The neonate lies away from the dam for the first three weeks and thereafter joins a nursery crèche of calves of similar age. This behaviour continues after the herd is released into the paddock. Calves show a marked preference for lying out close to tall weeds and vertical enclosure walls. On several occasions, individual females left the adults to join the crèche group.

Calves nibble at soil within a few days of birth and are eating grass and supplemental food by three weeks of age. Suckling occurs in bouts of 30 to 120 seconds, several times per day, and there is often social facilitation. Older calves suckle while resting on the carpal joints and often prod the udder, sometimes causing the dam to move off. Full weaning occurs between the ages of five and ten months.

No data have been collected at Edinburgh on the age of sexual maturity in males. Of the females, F D reached puberty and conceived when aged 18 months, while F A was served at the age of 25½ months. Although F 05 first displayed behavioural oestrus at 18 months, she did not conceive until 14 months later.

Interspecific Contact

There were remarkably few interactions between the species, although there were some incidents involving one male Oryx and the Lechwe. No agonistic interactions were observed between Lechwe and any of the female Oryx, even when in full oestrus, nor was fighting observed between any of the Lechwe and Oryx M 2.

Interesting interspecific interactions occurred in August 1983, when two Zebra mares took a close interest in a newborn Oryx calf F A. The primiparous dam, F 56, appeared unconcerned as the mares herded F A towards the tall weeds, where she lay up for her first three weeks.

Unusual Behaviour

A 1985 calf, M R12, carries extremely mis-shapen horns which were damaged at five weeks of age, when the horn buds are especially sensitive. After his injury, he was visibly troubled by flies surrounding his horns and was frequently found lying some distance from the other three crèching calves. He and the three other 1985 calves were weaned and sent to Marwell Zoo and subsequently he went to Tunisia with two of these calves. Once in Tunisia, M R12's condition deteriorated and he is now the lowest-ranking male and the second lowest overall (Bertram, this volume, page 143). No abnormal behaviour was observed in M G10, the other Edinburgh male that went to Tunisia. His highly aggressive biting behaviour, observed in Tunisia (Wacher, 1986a), is assumed to have arisen after his departure from Edinburgh.

During the 1986 calving period in the pens, water consumption by the Oryx was measured as 5 litres/Oryx/day for adults. This compares with a figure of 2.4 litres for six-to-seven-month-old calves in Tunisia in December 1985 (Wacher, 1986a). In June 1986, an abnormal drinking behaviour was observed. Female 54 threw her head back with a mouthful of water, slowly 'gurgling it playfully'. This behaviour was also performed by F A on 5 February 1986.

Although all adults use their horns to thrash thistles and other vegetation, dropping to the carpals when excited, only F 59 has demonstrated a proficiency with the use of her wide-spread horns to hook down low-hanging branches of Beech trees *Fagus sylvatica*. This behaviour has also been recorded from F G10 in Tunisia (Gordon and Wacher, 1987).

Chewing of bones, dropped by crows, has been noted occasionally, twice occurring in the spring. Bone-chewing may provide minerals in short supply in the paddock (Leuthold, 1977). Both F 56 on 13 April 1983 and F 54 on 28 March 1985 were carrying calves in their last four months of pregnancy, a time of high metabolic need.

Vocalisations

Six types of sound were distinguished: adult contact, juvenile contact and calf contact calls, adult snorts, calf 'moans' and dam 'purr' calls. The fundamental frequency range of calf calls is higher than that of juveniles and, as the juvenile calls approach adult ones in structure, the fundamental frequency and frequency of the first formant decrease. Similarly, the fundamental frequency of calf calls is higher than that of the juveniles.

Vocalisations were louder from isolated animals. When denied access to the paddock or feed, adult calls often formed part of a call sequence which could be related to the degree of arousal. Later in

Table 13.2: Measurements taken from sonagrams made from recordings of captive Oryx

Animal	Age class when recorded	Number of calls analysed	Mean of fundamental (Hz)	Range of fundamental (Hz)	Range of first formant (Hz)	Range of second formant (Hz)	Range of third formant (Hz)
F 56	Adult	14	88	54 – 112	400 – 700	1000 – 1500	1650 – 3400
F 54	"	12	72	60 – 80	400 – 700	900 – 1500	1400 – 2900
F 57	"	8	75	60 – 96	300 – 500	1050 – 1700	1600 – 2800
F 59	"	5	70	68 – 72	200 – 300	1050 – 1400	1450 – 2050
F 60	"	0	–	–	–	–	–
M 2	"	3	81	80 – 84	150 – 250	1000 – 1200	1300 – 1700
M 3	"	1	96	96	250	1150	1750
F A	Juvenile	4	102	80 – 112	500 – 700	1450 – 1850	2700 – 3700
F A	Calf	4	172	144 – 192	300 – 550	1300 – 1900	2250 – 2850
F 05	"	0	–	–	–	–	–
F R4	"	1	176	176	1350	2050	3000
F D	"	8	217	208 – 224	450 – 950	1200 – 1700	1750 – 2400
M 4	"	11	159	120 – 200	120 – 200	1400 – 2800	1750 – 3650

the sequence, the calls became louder, and longer in duration, the time interval between successive calls decreased and the frequency range was lower. If one individual exhibited high arousal calling, other animals tended to join in. Oestrus females were especially vocal. Bulls also vocalised when unable to herd females.

Figure 13.1: Sonagram of vocalisation recorded from F D on 4 September 1984

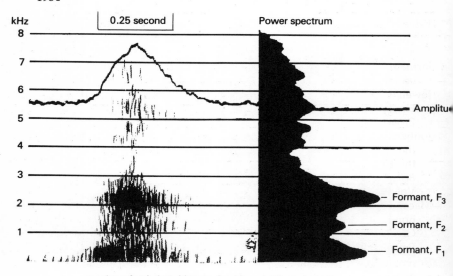

number of striations/time = fundamental frequency, f_0

Calves gave a very distinctive contact call when separated from their dams, or when disturbed from their lying-out positions. The responses of females to calf calls were related to the age of the calf. When calves were under seven days old, all parous females looked in the direction of the calf; when an older calf called, only its dam looked up towards the calf, and sometimes vocalised and approached. Dams were also observed to call, eliciting a response from the lying-out calves. The 'moan' call was given towards the end of the weaning process by the calf as its dam turned away. The 'purr' call was heard from dams only when licking their neonates. Some individual animals (F 56, F 54, F 57, F A and F D) were especially vocal and are therefore well represented in the analysis.

Calls of individual adults were very noisy and variable, and it proved difficult to measure parameters that would enable comparisons to be made. From calf calls of similar volume and duration, however, it was possible to make sonagrams for comparison between and within individuals. It was possible, by examination of the power spectra, to assign unlabelled sonagrams correctly to the caller.

In April 1983, swellings were first noticed in the necks of some of the Oryx. These swellings developed, and by May 1983 those of F F60, 57 and 54 were bi-lobed. Vocal activity had by this time become quite frequent and, in some cases, loud. After her first calf was born, F 56 became much more vocal and her larynx increased in size relative to those of the other oryx. The male, too, became more vocal and the pitch of his calls became lower. When the male was removed, his larynx and that of F 56 appeared to be the largest. However, the isolation imposed upon F 56 through 1984, following her horn removal and leg injury, resulted in her losing rank and at the same time becoming less vocal. By October 1984, the two top-ranking animals, F 54 and F 57, had the largest larynxes and even the relatively quiet F 59 appeared to have a larger larynx than F 56.

Discussion

Activities

The preference of standing and lying Oryx for a particular quadrant in the summer is clearly related to its level south-facing aspect receiving the most direct sunlight. In the winter, their habit of standing in the shelter of the housing areas, particularly in the afternoon, may induce keepers to give them access to their housing sooner than might otherwise occur. Scores for this area are high in winter, partly because observations started at 09.00 hours when the herd was slow to move after being put out into the paddock, particularly on cold, wet or misty mornings. Once out, the herd often moves rapidly from the housing area to a relatively sheltered area containing a variety of food plants, including some browse. Owing in part to the absence of the bull, and to the crèching of calves, Oryx spent more time lying in the summer. This is revealed in an elevated proportion of their time engaged in standing and lying (see Table 13.3). However, considerable time was spent standing in the winter, often under the trees sheltering from rain. Significantly more time was spent moving, which probably reflects the need to keep warm and the bull's herding behaviour in the winter.

In spite of a greatly increased consumption of hay, Oryx spend more time grazing in the winter, using their small mouths to select nutrient-rich winter vegetation. Although much greater than for Zebra, this increase is not as marked as that for Lechwe (see Table 13.3). Research into their gut physiology in the laboratory and the feeding ecology of the related Fringe-eared Oryx *Oryx beisa callotis* (Stanley Price, 1985) suggests that Oryx extract more nutrients than even sheep from low-quality diets. Interestingly, the non-ruminant Zebras are unable to extract much at all from grazing in the winter and rely almost exclusively on the provided hay and supplemental diet.

Although little is known of the time budgets of wild Scimitar-horned Oryx, data are provided for comparison with the figures for one-year-old juveniles in May 1986 in a 10-hectare paddock in

Table 13.3: Average times spent by Zebra, Oryx and Lechwe in each of three major activities as a proportion of the total time engaged in these activities

Observed in July and August 1985			
	Zebra	Oryx	Lechwe
Standing/lying	20.3%	65.8%	86.7%
Moving	19.7%	14.4%	2.8%
Grazing	60.0%	19.8%	10.5%
Total	100%	100%	100%

Observed in January and February 1983			
	Zebra	Oryx	Lechwe
Standing/lying	42.6%	54.5%	44.7%
Moving	49.5%	23.5%	29.7%
Grazing	7.9%	22.0%	25.6%
Total	100%	100%	100%

Observation in Tunisia 1986 (juvenile Oryx)	
	Oryx
Lying	29.0%
Moving	15.3%
Grazing	55.7%
Total	100%

Tunisia (Wacher, 1986b). Table 13.3 shows the total time spent in the three major activities (standing/lying, moving and grazing) over the 15-hour observation periods. The activity cycles of both groups are strongly influenced by supplemental feeding. A major difference is that the Edinburgh Oryx are locked up at night and are therefore unable to graze at that time. In both situations, the Oryx adopted a three-bout feeding cycle, but, as the vegetation in the Tunisian enclosure diminished, the mid-afternoon resting period was cut out (Bertram, this volume, page 142).

Reproductive Behaviour

Although physiological data on the 21- to 22-day oestrus cycle of oryx has not yet been reported, it closely resembles that of the domestic cow (Durrant, 1983). The first of two waves of follicular growth occurs during the four- to five-day follicular phase. The second wave occurs towards the end of the subsequent 15–17-day luteal phase, which culminates in behavioural oestrus. During fertile cycles, ovulation follows around ten hours later (Rowlands and Weir, 1984). Parturition dates in 1985 and 1986 suggest that some synchronisation of oestrus occurred during the preceding autumns, which may account for the confusing mounting combinations that were observed. Although the lip-curl display (*flehmen*) among females may not be closely related to oestrus, Pfeifer (1985) found that increases in the frequency of mounting attempts were accompanied by increases in the occurrence of *flehmen*.

The median gestation period calculated at Edinburgh is very close to the mean (248 days, S.D. 7.1) for seven pregnancies at Hannover Zoo (Dittrich, 1972). The time interval between 30 births of successive calves born to five individual females at Los Angeles Zoo and San Diego Wild Animal Park ranged from 200 to 325 days, with a median of 276 days (Dolan, 1976). Although Oryx cows may come into oestrus a few days after parturition (Newby, this volume, page 151), the considerable individual variation reported by Knowles and Oliver (1975) may be due to differential inhibitory effects of individual suckling frequencies.

The high number of daytime births confirms that the herd is relatively undisturbed when kept in during the calving period. Thus, pre-parturient restlessness probably does not reflect maternal efforts to withdraw from the herd, but rather a physical discomfort that can be relieved by proceeding with parturition.

Although it is usual for ungulates to calve in recumbency (Edwards and Broom, 1982), on two occasions calves had been born to below the head when the dam stood and completed parturition. Edwards and Broom (1982) list functions that have been suggested for maternal licking, emphasising the strong attraction of parturient cows to birth fluids and their role in calf recognition. No calves at Edinburgh have been rejected by their dams.

The weight of Edinburgh calves was similar to the mean of 10.37 kilos for four calves born at Hannover Zoo (Dittrich, 1969 and 1979). The preference of calves is for lying-out locations which offer both shade and shelter from wind and rain. By increasing peer interactions, crèching benefits the social development of calves and at the same time necessitates an unambiguous system of individual recognition. Since the crèche may be watched over by just one adult, the system of individual recognition should be expected to operate over some distance.

Since calves may hold a teat in their mouths without sucking, it is most important to observe contractions at the calf's throat when checking that suckling behaviour is normal. In view of the potential advantages for a dam suckling closely related but strange calves in the crèche group while the calves' dams may be far away drinking or feeding, it is perhaps surprising that this has been observed only once, by a very low-ranking dam.

To date, all females born at Edinburgh have reached sexual maturity later than those at San Diego Wild Animal Park, for which puberty has been established at 10 to 13 months (Dolan, 1976). The age of sexual maturity in males has been estimated at Marwell Zoo to be 12 to 16 months (Peter Small, pers. comm.).

Interspecific Contact

Aggression may not be surprising for captive animals that would normally live peacefully (Hediger, 1950; Eisenberg and Kleiman 1977) and several factors may be involved. Firstly, the frequency and consequences of such aggression may be high between related species of ungulate (Walther, 1964). If so, the overlap in preferred grazing areas of Oryx and Lechwe probably contributed to the fighting between the two by bringing them into greater contact. Secondly, the individual Oryx involved, M 3, had been isolated previously for 29 months and this may have had some effect upon his subsequent behaviour. Thirdly, most of the escalated fighting occurred when the total number of Lechwe in the exhibit was high.

The superiority of Lechwe bulls in fights with oryx males may be related to different fighting techniques, and to Lechwe possessing much thicker horns, neck musculature and skin along the flanks (Walther, 1974; Schuster, 1976). High-intensity Lechwe fights involve attempts to gore the flanks (Schuster, 1976), which, in Oryx, are poorly protected by thin skin. Furthermore, each species' ritual preliminaries are likely to be misunderstood by non-specifics. The low-level sparring characteristics of Oryx fighting may provoke a Lechwe bull into a high-intensity attack, for which the oryx's response of ritually dropping on to the knees is not the best defence. A particular fighting technique observed frequently in the Edinburgh Oryx herd, over-shoulder stabbing, appears to be unsuccessful against an excited Lechwe. Finally, the tactic of following a lateral approach is likely to result in severe injuries to the Oryx's flanks from a frontal Lechwe attack.

Vocalisations

High-arousal calling suggests that vocalisation may be used as an indicator of stress. This promising area of study has not been fully investigated.

The fact that it is possible to distinguish between the calls of calves, and that dams respond to their own calves' calls, strongly suggests that females are able to distinguish their own calves by voice. Espmark (1971 and 1975) points out the advantages of such recognition systems for migratory species with undistinctively marked calves. The critical period for such vocal recognition has not yet been investigated.

Because their small mouthparts permit the selection of dispersed nutrient-rich grasses (Field, 1975), the spacing behaviour of feeding Oryx may result in some individuals becoming isolated. During the day, the conspicuous adult coat markings serve as flags which maintain the cohesion of social groups. At night, however, Oryx communicate by low contact calls (Stanley Price, 1986) which are likely to carry some distance in their wild habitat. Loud calling may have arisen in Scimitar-horned Oryx with a relaxation of selective pressures, in the absence of predators in captivity and possibly in the wild habitat as well.

With increasing age and social rank, the external appearance of the larynx enlarges. Owing to the inverse logarithmic relationship between body mass and the lowest-frequency sound produced (August and Anderson, 1987), an age-related change in formant structure is not surprising. Further investigation is required to determine whether the frequency characteristics of oryx vocalisations are related to rank.

Products mentioned in the text

(A) Grovax serovaccine supplied by Hoechst.
(B) Dairy pellets (18% protein), BOCM Silcock.
(C) Vitamin E pellets, Special Diet Services.

Acknowledgements

The assistance is acknowledged of the staff of The Royal Zoological Society of Scotland, in particular Sheila Brydone, as well as the Phonetics Department and members of the Zoology Department of the University of Edinburgh.

References

August, P.V., and Anderson, J.G.T. (1987) Mammal sounds and motivation—structural rules: A test of the hypothesis. *J. Mamm. 68* (1): 1–9.

Cave-Browne, Ann M. (1983) An ecological study of the three species of ungulate in the African exhibit at Edinburgh Zoo. The Royal Zoological Society of Scotland, *Annual Report* (1983).

Dittrich, L. (1969) Birth weights and weight increases of African antelopes born at Hannover Zoo. *Int. Zoo Ybk 9*: 118–20.

Dittrich, L. (1972) Gestation periods and age of sexual maturity of some African antelopes. *Int. Zoo Ybk 12*: 184–7.

Dittrich, L. (1979) Some further weights of African antelopes born at Hannover Zoo. *Int. Zoo Ybk 19*: 201.

Dolan, J.M. (1976) The Arabian oryx, its destruction, captive husbandry and propagation. *Int. Zoo Ybk 16*: 230–9.

Durrant, B.S. (1983) Reproductive studies of the oryx. *Zoo Biology 2*: 191–7.

Edwards, S.A., and Broom, D.M. (1982) Behavioural interactions of dairy cows with their newborn calves and the effects of parity. *An. Behav. 30*: 525–35.

Eisenberg, J., and Kleiman, D. (1977) The usefulness of behaviour studies in developing captive breeding programmes for mammals. *Int. Zoo Ybk 17*: 81–9.

Espmark, Y. (1971) Individual recognition by voice in Reindeer, *Rangifer tarandus*, mother-young relationship. Field observation and playback experiments. *Behaviour 40*: 295–301.

Scimitar-horned Oryx at Edinburgh Zoo

Espmark, Y. (1975) Individual characteristics in the calls of Reindeer, *Rangifer tarandus* calves. *Behaviour 54*: 50–9.

Field, C.R. (1975) Climate and the food habits of ungulates on Galana Ranch. *E. Afr. Wildl. J. 13*: 203–20.

Flach, E.J. (1986) Gastro-intestinal parasitism in ungulates at Edinburgh Zoo. The Royal Zoological Society of Scotland, *Annual Report* (1986).

Gill, J.P. (1985) Vocalization of a herd of Scimitar-horned Oryx (*Oryx dammah*). The Royal Zoological Society of Scotland, *Annual Report* (1985).

Gordon, I., and Wacher, T. (1987) Unpublished reports to Zoological Society of London.

Hediger, H. (1950) *Wild Animals in Captivity*. Butterworth, London.

Jones, D.M. (1985) The care of exotic animals. *Symp. Zool. Soc. Lond. 54*: 89–102.

Knowles, J.M., and Oliver, W.L.R. (1975) Breeding and husbandry of Scimitar-horned oryx at Marwell Zoo. *Int. Zoo Ybk 15*: 184–7.

Leuthold, W. (1977) *African Ungulates*. Springen, Berlin, Heidelberg, New York.

O'Connor, S.M. (1986) Activity cycles of the southern White Rhinoceros, *Ceratotherium s. simum* in captivity: Implications for management. *Int. Zoo Ybk 24/25*: 297–302.

Pfeifer, S. (1985) Flehmen and dominance among captive adult Scimitar-horned oryx, *Oryx dammah*. *J. Mamm. 66* (1): 160–3.

Rowlands, I.W., and Weir, B.J. (1984) Mammals: Non-primate eutherians. In Lamming, G.E. (ed.), *Marshall's Physiology of Reproduction*, Vol. 1: 455–658.

Schuster, R.H. (1976) Lekking behaviour in Kafue Lechwe. *Science 192*: 1240–2.

Stanley Price, M.R. (1985) Game domestication for animal production in Kenya: Feeding trials with Oryx, Zebu cattle and sheep under controlled conditions. *J. Agric. Sci. Camb. 104*: 367–74.

Stanley Price, M.R. (1986) The re-introduction of Arabian Oryx, *Oryx leucoryx* into Oman, Int. Zoo Ybk 24/25: 179–188.

Wacher, T. (1986a) Unpublished report No. 1 to Zoological Society of London.

Wacher, T. (1986b) Unpublished report No. 2 to Zoological Society of London.

Walther, F.R. (1964) Ethological aspects of keeping different species of ungulates together in captivity. *Int. Zoo Ybk 5: 1–3*.

Walther, F.R. (1974) Some reflections on expressive behaviour in combats and courtship in certain horned ungulates. In Geist, V., and Walther, F.R. (eds.), *The Behaviour of Ungulates and Its Relation to Management*. IUCN Publ. No. 24: pp. 56–106.

14. Re-introducing Scimitar-horned Oryx into Tunisia

Brian C.R. Bertram

Introduction

Early in December 1985, a group of ten young Scimitar-horned Oryx *Oryx dammah* was sent from Britain to Tunisia to be re-introduced into the wild in the Bou-Hedma National Park. This report describes the programme and summarises the progress up to 18 months later, at the time of the Arabian Oryx *Oryx leucoryx* programme's 25th-year celebration.

A number of comparisons should immediately be made with the highly successful Arabian Oryx programme. Firstly, we have been able to benefit from the experience with the Arabian Oryx. The importance of establishing stable groups and of careful monitoring was well accepted, and there was a general expectation that a re-introduction could succeed, whereas a few years earlier there might have been much more scepticism. Secondly, the first steps in Scimitar-horned Oryx captive conservation were taken much earlier in the decline of the species. As a result, the captive population is much larger, and more heathly genetically, and potentially more individuals are available. Thirdly, the logistics are easier because the distances and areas involved are much smaller. Fourthly, the programme is inevitably much less well funded. And, finally, the main problem to be overcome is that of re-establishing a habitat, whereas in Arabia, it is one of protecting a re-introduced species in an otherwise little-altered habitat.

The Tunisian Habitat

The Bou-Hedma National Park is situated roughly in the centre of Tunisia, at the northern edge of the arid zone which includes the southern half of the country. It is categorised as semi-desert with extensive grazing. The area receives 100–200 millimetres of rainfall

136

per year. The east-west range of mountains which form the National Park's northern boundary rise to 1,200 metres. They force upwards the moisture-laden north winds from the Mediterranean and receive the resulting rain. The originally well-forested mountains release this rain water via springs and streams, both to the north and to the south.

With a hot climate and with abundant water, the area used to be very fertile and well inhabited. In places, the ground is littered with worked flint implements dating back to prehistoric times perhaps 20,000 years ago. Under the Romans, when the area was part of the productive cereal-growing region known as the granary of the Roman Empire, there was extensive terracing and irrigation, of which signs still remain. There is an astonishingly well-preserved section of aquaduct 6 metres high, carrying a water channel some 5 metres wide and over 1 metre deep out from the foothills.

Over recent centuries, the country has become more arid throughout, with the increasing desertification of the edges of the Sahara to the south and the ravages of a growing and displaced human population from the north. The tree cover on Bou-Hedma's line of mountains has been completely destroyed in the past 200 years. There is less rain, but it runs off faster, causing both gully and surface erosion. Attempts at cultivation of cereals hasten the process, as does the trampling and grazing of herds of domestic stock—camels, sheep and goats. In places, the exposed roots of dwarf shrubs show that five or more centimetres of surface soil has been lost in the past few years.

The Bou-Hedma National Park

Delineation of the National Park area at Bou-Hedma was initiated some 50 years ago and today it covers an area of about 120 km^2. About one quarter of this is the mountain terrain to the north, the rest being relatively flat, divided by slight drainage lines which run north-south.

Designation did not result in effective protection until recently. As a result, part of the park area is still occupied by human beings. In the 1960s, a tree-planting scheme was established by the United Nations Food and Agriculture Organisation, and scattered eucalyptus and other trees date from that time.

In 1977, 2,400 hectares of the National Park were made a Total

Protection Zone, as a result of the initiative of the Direction des Forêts of the Ministry of Agriculture in Tunisia. Agreements were struck with the local people that they would stay out of the Total Protection Zone in return for 20-year leases on the rest of the park area outside it. The agreements and the meagre wire fence delineating the Total Protection Zone have been effective, and within it a vigorous programme of habitat rehabilitation has been established.

The effects on the vegetation of the exclusion of domestic hoofstock have been dramatic. Over ten years, chewed ankle-high rootstocks have grown into 2–3-metre high *Acacia tortilis* trees, with impressive thorns. Dwarf shrubs similarly are growing and increasing the ground cover, now to some 17%. The new vegetation slows the wind, so producing more stable microclimates and preventing all the leaves from blowing away. A leaf-litter layer is appearing in places, and with it more fertile soil and the opportunity for less hardy plants to germinate. Increasing numbers and variety of insects can survive now and in consequence so can more birds, as well as reptiles and small mammals. The mixture of bushes, dwarf shrubs and grasses will provide ample browse and grazing for re-introduced antelopes.

As well as simply allowing the vegetation to regenerate naturally, staff of the Direction des Forêts have also been taking an active role, assisted by the German Technical Co-operation Agency (GTZ). Many experimental schemes are being worked on, including clogging drainage lines and planting trees of a variety of local species. Nurseries near the springs produce thousands of tree seedlings. These require planting in holes deep enough to break through the surface crust layer, and large enough to collect the small amount of rainfall which can be expected. The space-age water-retaining substance Aquastore is being used to hold water for the seedlings to make use of, but individual irrigation may still be necessary for two or three years.

The results of all this effort are impressive, but they are not immediately dramatic or attention-drawing, as would be the presence among this newly restored vegetation of the original herbivore inhabitants of the area—Oryx, Addax *Addax nasomaculatus*, gazelles *Gazella* spp. and Ostriches *Struthio camelus*. It was partly in order to reinforce the fine rehabilitation work, as well as to restore as full a complement of the indigenous fauna that belonged there, that the Direction des Forêts approached sections of the international zoo community in 1985 with a request for animals.

The Conservation Position of Scimitar-horned Oryx

The Scimitar-horned Oryx used to be widely distributed in North Africa around the edges of the Sahara. It stretched from Morocco and Senegal across to Egypt and Sudan (*Red Data Book*, 1976). Its decline in the past couple of centuries has been as dramatic as it has been appalling (Newby, this volume, pp. 146–166). The fundamental problem is, of course, too many people and their various activities, often uncontrolled. Desertification, competition with domestic herbivores, disturbance and hunting have all contributed. Scimitar-horned Oryx are reported to have disappeared from Tunisia in 1902, and have similarly disappeared from most other countries in their range. A decade ago, a total population of only 5,000–7,000 was believed to exist, mainly in Chad but also in Mali and Niger (*Red Data Book*, 1976). Now perhaps only dozens, if any, still survive (Newby, this volume, pp. 159–160).

Fortunately, the likely future threats to the species had been recognised by the captive-conservation community some 20 years ago. At that time, when the world population still numbered several thousand, a few dozen animals were taken from the wild and used to found the present captive stock. The species has thrived in captivity and is estimated to number some 2,000 now; about 900 of them are included in the North American Regional Studbook for Scimitar-horned Oryx (Rost, 1985) and there are at least 250 in zoos outside North America.

The British Isles population is derived from the 16 animals which Mr John Knowles imported and brought to Marwell in 1971 when establishing the new Marwell Zoological Park. They have done well, have risen to 64 in number (after many exports) and are currently accommodated at Marwell, Whipsnade, Edinburgh, Fota (Dublin) and Chichester (private). They are all owned jointly by the Marwell Preservation Trust Ltd and The Zoological Society of London.

Selection of Individual Animals for Tunisia

Ten animals were considered an appropriate number in view of the size of the facilities available, the costs of keeping the animals, and of transporting them. It was felt that this number would suffice for the pilot nature of the project at this stage, yet would form a useful nucleus of a successful population. Five males and five females were decided on. A higher proportion of females would have allowed faster population growth, but would have put more valuable animals at risk; males are more available. From the Arabian Oryx programme it was known that an equal sex ratio could work well and that other males in oryx groups serve useful functions.

It was not possible to develop an age-structured herd in the time and space available; therefore it was considered better to supply a group of young animals which could be integrated early with one another with few problems, and in which the social structure would develop gradually. There was also the important point that young animals could be transported much more cheaply and conveniently, for two reasons: that several could be enclosed together in a single large crate, and that such crates were still low enough to be fitted in through the aircraft doors on one of the regular flights available cheaply.

The genetic composition of the group was considered to achieve the best compromise of a diverse genetic base, both in the ten colonists for Tunisia and in the remaining population in Britain. In the event, this resulted in seven young animals being selected from Marwell Zoo and three from Edinburgh Zoo.

Transport to Bou-Hedma

The ten young Oryx, assembled at Marwell, were put into two large crates 2.7 metres × 1.5 metres × 1.5 metres, with five animals in each crate. In these they settled down at once. They lay during most of the journey, by lorry from Marwell to Portsmouth, ferry to Le Havre, lorry to Paris, *Tunis Air* flight to Tunis and lorry to Bou-Hedma. They were released 48 and 63 hours after being crated.

Management at Bou-Hedma

A group of eight reception pens made of light-stock mesh had been constructed at Bou-Hedma and the Oryx, on arrival, were released into one of the larger of these, about 600 square metres in area. They remained there for a 4½-month acclimatisation period and then were released into a 10-hectare pre-release enclosure in which they have spent 14 months.

The animals are allowed back into their reception pen for about three hours each morning and there supplied with low-quality hay followed by about 1 kilo each of concentrate pellets. They are then released again to forage for the rest of the day on the natural vegetation in the 10-hectare enclosure.

Other species are also being re-introduced at the same time. Two groups of Addax from Hannover Zoo arrived in late 1985 and early 1986, and have been following the same daily routine, being fed in their two reception pens separate from the Oryx. Three Ostriches, received from within Tunisia in early 1986, complete the species being allowed to use the 10-hectare enclosure. In addition, the other reception pens have been holding two groups of two and six Barbary Sheep *Ammotragus lervia* and a group of five Dorcas Gazelles *Gazella dorcas*, all intended for re-introduction elsewhere later.

Monitoring

Outline records of the major events in the Oryx and other groups are maintained by the staff of the Direction des Forêts at Bou-Hedma. In addition, we have been able to arrange four brief monitoring visits to obtain detailed information on the development of the animals' social organisation. These have been conducted by Dr T.J. Wacher (9–21 December 1985), Dr Wacher (21 April–11 May 1986), Dr Wacher and Dr I.J. Gordon (30 November –7 December 1986) and Dr Gordon and Dr B.C.R. Bertram (1–10 May 1987). Detailed reports from each visit have been produced and circulated to interested parties (Wacher, 1986a, 1986b; Gordon and Wacher, 1986; Gordon and Bertram, 1987).

Monitoring individual animals' progress depends on being able to recognise those individuals. Each Oryx was fitted with a colour-ed tag in each ear before transport; three of these were lost during the first five months, but the remaining 17 have stayed in place for a further 13 months so far. In practice, individual identification at a distance is actually achieved using natural features such as markings, marks and horn irregularities, with ear-tags being valuable for confirmation. The detail of the shape of the brown patch on the nose has remained virtually constant over the past 18 months.

During the monitoring visits, observations were made on activity budgets, on interactions between individuals and on their spacing patterns, on interactions with the other species, and on their feeding and effects on the vegetation available.

Results

Detailed results are given in the reports from the four monitoring visits so far, and the following account summarises these.

1. *Adjustment*. The animals have adjusted to the change of climate and habitat without problems. They use the shade and water sources as appropriate.

2. *Condition*. The animals have remained in good health throughout. They do not have a visible tick burden. Faecal samples examined have revealed no gut parasites. Visual assessments of condition after 18 months indicated that three of them could be classified as in medium to poor condition, but the rest ranged from medium to excellent.

3. *Reproduction*. Oestrus behaviour was observed in three of the females in the autumn of 1986, and three calves are expected in the summer of 1987.

4. *Grouping*. Within three hours of emerging from their transport crates, the ten animals were sitting together in an outward-facing radial group typical of wild Oryx. They move around in their enclosure as a loose group, usually all being within about 150 metres of one another, and they tend to synchronise their bouts of feeding, movement and resting.

5. *Activity patterns*. To some extent, these are controlled by the feeding and separation regime. In general, the animals are fairly inactive in the morning, waiting to be allowed in to their supplementary food. They rest in the reception pen after feeding. On release again, the animals generally go straight to drink, then forage for two or three hours, then rest for an hour or so, then forage for the rest of the day on the now sparse natural vegetation in the 10-hectare enclosure. They are covering 2–3 kilometres per day.

6. *Dominance*. One male (No. 1) is clearly dominant and has been since the moment of arrival. Although all the animals were born within ten weeks of one another in the summer of 1985, two years later he is noticeably larger and distinctly more impressive than any of the others. From the beginning, he horn-rubbed and horn-threshed the vegetation more than any other animal. He spends less time feeding than the other animals, but because of his height

and horn length he can reach or hook down more browse than the others. He can also displace others from their food sources. He is most often closest to most other individuals and he initiates many more interactions than any other animal.

7. *Dominance hierarchies*. There is a linear dominance hierarchy among the males, with almost no reversals, and which has not changed in the past 18 months. One male (No. 6, from Edinburgh) complicated the initial picture by his tendency to nip with his teeth the rear ends of the other animals, but that behaviour had disappeared within four months and No. 6 is now second in the hierarchy. The females interact among one another much less than do the males, but again there is a clear linear hierarchy among them, with very few reversals. At first, some females were dominant over the lower-ranking males, but now every male ranks above all the females. The lowest-ranking male (No. 8) is an individual with a grotesquely twisted horn. His low rank may be because his horns are less effective for sparring with; but he is also the only individual who is inbred to any significant extent (0.22 compared with less than 0.1 for all the others). It is possible that inbreeding contributes to the vulnerability of horns to accidental damage.

8. *Growth*. There have been marked differences in the growth rates of different individuals. The dominant male (No. 1) is taller by 5 centimetres and looks older than any other male. By contrast, the two subordinate females (Nos. 3 and 5) are somewhat smaller than the other females and still look almost like yearlings.

9. *Grouping*. Associations of individuals are not random, but are not at all close. Animals no longer associate preferentially with others from the same zoo. Males generally tend to be nearest neighbours to other males, and females to females. The two subordinate females are the most consistent nearest neighbours. The second-ranking female (No. 2) tends to be the furthest from other animals and she is the most likely to be leading the foraging wanderings.

10. *Diet*. When foraging in the 10-hectare pre-release enclosure, the Oryx were initially feeding mainly on grasses. Some 90% of their bites were of grasses of nine species, mainly *Cenchrus*. They were more catholic in their tastes than the Addax, which fed 96% on grasses. The proportion of grasses available in the 10-hectare

enclosure and therefore in the diet of both species has declined markedly over the year.

11. *Developing feeding techniques.* The newly-arrived oryx were cautiously adventurous in sampling the unfamiliar vegetation suddenly available to them. They sniffed at new plants first and then sampled them. Some they first thrashed with their horns before scenting and tasting. Some they then rejected, particularly the known noxious species. There were signs of learning from one another by observation. They have become adept at picking off *Acacia* leaves from among the thorns. They use their horns to hook down twigs which they are otherwise unable to reach.

12. *Effects on vegetation.* As a result of a year's feeding by 21 herbivores (among them the ten Oryx), the vegetation inside the 10-hectare enclosure has been drastically knocked back. Of the 44 species of grasses, herbs, shrubs and trees identified inside 'the enclosure, 21 have been hard hit (especially the grasses); only seven have remained uneaten, and half of these have been damaged by horning.

Conclusions

1. The habitat-rehabilitation programme at Bou-Hedma is proving very successful and deserves further recognition, support and encouragement.

2. The transfer of a nucleus herd of animals from Britain to Tunisia has been achieved successfully and economically.

3. It is very encouraging so far that a group of naïve young captive-born animals can so quickly and so well adjust to the new climate and food.

4. It is striking how smoothly an apparently natural Oryx social organisation can develop among a group of young naïve animals, and how quickly, effectively and peacefully the dominance hierarchies are established.

5. Small-scale re-introduction projects with Scimitar-horned Oryx should be practicable over much of the species' former range, provided that adequately protected areas can be made available.

6. Monitoring of such projects provides a great deal of information of value to future projects.

Acknowledgements

Most of the data on which the results section of this chapter is based have been collected by Dr Tim Wacher and Dr Iain Gordon, to whom I am most grateful. So am I to the Direction des Forêts of the Ministry of Agriculture of the Government of Tunisia, for permissions and for the assistance given by their staff and their GTZ advisers, particularly M. Kacem, M. Hosni, Herr Muller and Herr Waibel. Funding for the monitoring visits has been provided by the Fauna and Flora Preservation Society, to whom we are indebted. Transport of the animals to Tunisia was generously funded by the Fondation Internationale pour la Sauvegarde du Gibier. We are grateful also to *Tunis Air* for transporting animals and observers at much-reduced rates. The Zoological Society of London and Marwell Preservation Trust Ltd donated the animals free of charge.

Postscript

The animals were released from the 10-hectare enclosure into the Total Protection Zone on 6 July 1987, and appeared to be behaving very sensibly in their new environment. A calf has been born.

References

Gordon, I.J., and Wacher, T.J. (1986) *The Re-introduction of Scimitar-horned Oryx (Oryx dammah) from the United Kingdom to Tunisia.* Report No. 3. Mimeograph: Zoological Society of London, pp. 1–15.

Gordon, I.J., and Bertram, B.C.R. (1987) *The Re-introduction of Scimitar-horned Oryx (Oryx dammah) from the United Kingdom to Tunisia.* Report No. 4. Mimeograph: Zoological Society of London, pp. 1–22.

Red Data Book (1976) Scimitar-horned Oryx. Loose-leaf page in *Red Data Book*, Vol. 1. Mammalia. International Union for Conservation of Nature, Morges, Switzerland.

Rost, A.F. (1985) *North American Regional Studbook 1985 for Scimitar-horned Oryx.* Published by Friends of the Zoo, Dickerson Park Zoo, Spring-field, Missouri.

Wacher, T.J. (1986a) *The Re-introduction of Scimitar-horned Oryx (Oryx dammah) from the United Kingdom to Tunisia.* Mimeograph: Zoological Society of London, pp. 1–31.

Wacher, T.J. (1986b) *The Re-introduction of Scimitar-horned Oryx (Oryx dammah) from the United Kingdom to Tunisia.* Report No. 2. Mimeograph: Zoological Society of London, pp. 1–18.

15. Aridland Wildlife in Decline: the Case of the Scimitar-horned Oryx

John E. Newby

Introduction

It is often said that one of the fundamental differences between man and the other inhabitants of the planet we share is his ability to learn from experience in a rational way. The veracity of this statement takes a severe knock when we consider our disgraceful history of environmental conservation and our penchant for destroying the very fabric upon which our survival depends.

Twenty-five years ago, a group of motivated people made a concerted effort to save the White or Arabian Oryx *Oryx leucoryx* from extinction. The result of their efforts is well known to us all and is rightly quoted as a fine example of a conservation success. Yet we are constantly faced with similar examples of species on the brink of extinction. The subject of this paper, the Scimitar-horned Oryx *Oryx dammah*, is but one of many. It is today one of the rarest antelopes in the world and, short of a miracle, may within the next couple of years be extinct in the wild. That an obscure endemic fish or bird, occupying a tiny lake or patch of forest, disappears is certainly a loss but is by no stretch of the imagination improbable. But what of the Oryx, a large antelope that until recently inhabited a range of hundreds of thousands of square kilometres? The fact that it was also abundant underlines the scale and speed at which changes are affecting the maintenance of our planet's biological diversity.

To save the Scimitar-horned Oryx, we must once more, to quote Norman Myers (1979), 'send in the fire brigade' to rescue another hapless victim from extinction. How many 'Operation Oryx' can be mounted? How long can we go on tackling the problem of species extinction without confronting and mastering the causes rather than the results of such gross environmental carelessness? Or is it

inevitable? The answers to these questions are not only fundamental to the preservation of biological diversity but also to the
way in which we, as conservationists, tackle the problems before
us. The survival of such animals as the Scimitar-horned Oryx will
require a great deal more than the honest willingness of a small
number of conservation-minded individuals. Our limited number
and our limited access to limited funds severely restrict the action
we can take directly to save endangered wildlife.

One constantly gets the impression that the disappearance of
species is solely the result of man's indifference or carelessness.
Whilst recognising his key role in the Oryx's demise, mitigating
circumstances do exist that, whilst not acquitting man, certainly
put his role into a broader context of events.

Although this paper focuses on the Scimitar-horned Oryx, most
of what is presented is applicable to the other aridland species of
the Sahel and Sahara, many of which find themselves in a similar
predicament. The Arabian Oryx work has taught us a great deal
and we are undoubtedly in a position to apply this knowledge to
similar conservation problems. With this in mind, there is a hope
that, like its congener, the Scimitar-horned Oryx may benefit from
the same concerted effort to prevent its extinction in the wild.

A Prehistoric Background

Whilst the reasons for the recent decline in Oryx numbers are fairly
well documented, it is pertinent to begin the story several thousand years ago to understand better the long-term factors that
have influenced Oryx distribution and current conservation status.
During the past few years, a considerable amount of palaeoclima-
tological research has been prompted by the wave of recent
Sahelian droughts. Working in Africa, scientists are piecing
together evidence of long-term climatic trends, the better to understand currently observed conditions (Rognon, 1976; Maley, 1981;
Nicholson, 1982; Petit-Maire, 1984). Their work indicates the
following sequence of events.

During the Upper Pleistocene (18,000–12,000 BP), at a time
when Europe was in the throes of the last Ice Age, Africa
experienced a severe bout of desertification. The Sahara probably
extended up to 500 kilometres south of its current position,
reaching areas which are today wooded savanna with an annual

rainfall of 600–800 millimetres. The Holocene (10,000 BP-present) brought deglaciation and a pluvial period to Saharan Africa, accompanied by the formation of extensive inland seas (Palaeo-Chad, Taoudenni Basin, etc.) and the recolonisation of the entire desert by steppe and savanna formations (Petit-Maire, 1984). Maximum lake levels occurred 8,000–9,000 years ago and, although interrupted by an arid phase of about 1,000 years (c. 7,000 BP), the humid conditions lasted until about 4,000 BP. By 3,000 BP, it would appear that the Sahara Desert had once again expanded and for all intents and purposes had reached its present-day limits.

Whilst basing much of their work on the stratigraphy and nature of lake-bed sediments, the palaeoclimatologists have also studied human and animal remains as indicators of Quaternary climatic conditions. During the pluvial period, Stone Age man proliferated, sharing the Sahara's grasslands and lakes with a large variety of typical savanna animals—Elephant *Loxodonta africana*, Rhinoceros *Diceros bicornis*, Hippopotamus *Hippopotamus amphibius*, Giraffe *Giraffa camelopardalis*, Roan Antelope *Hippotragus equinus*, etc. (Mauny, 1957; McBurney, 1960; Petit-Maire, 1984) Of the Oryx and Addax *Addax nasomaculatus*, Petit-Maire is quite categoric: '. . . no sign of the large antelopes capable of surviving in an arid environment, such as the Oryx and the Addax, has been uncovered.' This is not really surprising when one considers that Stone Age man favoured the wetland habitats and that his middens would and do reflect locally-occurring, water-dependent species. However, it is safe to assume that the Oryx and Addax were there in the drier parts of the Saharan interior. Hufnagl (1972) mentions the existence of North African Oryx remains dating from the Pleistocene Age. The Oryx is also portrayed in rock engravings from Jebel Uweinat, dated at 5,000–6,000 BP. In general, prehistoric rock art clearly documents the changes in the composition of the Saharan fauna. Early scenes of savanna species give way to later representations of typical aridland species—Oryx, Addax, Barbary Sheep *Ammotragus lervia*—and, in many places, particularly suitable sites bear images of Elephant or Rhinoceros superimposed by scenes of Oryx, gazelles *Gazella* spp. or Ostrich *Struthio camelus*. By the time the Horse and Camel make their appearance in Saharan petroglyphs, the fauna portrayed is that of recent times. Whatever, it is also quite conceivable that both oryx and Addax were comparatively rare species during the pluvial period, increasing in numbers only when more arid habitat became available to them.

Ecology of the Scimitar-horned Oryx

Assuming that the Oryx has not undergone any significant changes in its ecology during the recent past, the end of the pluvial period, 3,000–4,000 years ago, would find it inhabiting the arid grasslands surrounding the Sahara. An indication of its probable distribution can be gleaned from Meigs' (1953) highly acclaimed work on the classification of the world's aridlands. Figure 15.1 is simplified from Meigs and shows the distribution of what he termed the 'Extremely Arid' and 'Arid' regions of North Africa. With an

Figure 15.1: Extremely arid (stippled) and arid (hatched) zones of North Africa (after Meigs, 1953)

annual rainfall of between 100 and 400 millimetres, Meigs' 'Arid' region can be considered suitable Oryx habitat.

Oryx are large, gregarious ruminants weighing up to 140 kilograms. Herds vary considerably in size, but most authors consider 15 to 30 to be normal in the wild (Brouin, 1950; Gillet, 1965; Newby, 1978). During migration or when concentrated in areas of good grazing, agglomerations of several hundred head may result (Malbrant, 1953; Gillet, 1969; Newby, 1978).

Principally grazers, Oryx feed on a wide variety of grasses and forbs (Gillet, 1965; Newby, 1978). The Sahelo-Saharan wet season (July-September) sees them feeding on freshly sprouted annuals. These same species form the bulk of the Oryx winter grazing too (November-February). During these cooler months, the Oryx reach the northern limits of their range, the Saharan fringes. With the onset of the hot season (March-June), the annual pastures dry up and Oryx start to look for green perennials, especially tussock grasses such as *Panicum turgidum*. The fallen pods of *Acacia tortilis* are also a favourite item, containing a high proportion of protein. As the hot season progresses, shade temperatures rise to 40°C to 45°C and all but the hardiest plants desiccate.

The annual quest for suitable food involves the Oryx in a cyclical pattern of seasonal movements, ranging from the desert fringes in the winter to the better-vegetated Sahelian dunelands in the hot season. In Chad, Oryx movements range over some 3–4° of latitude (13°–17°N), amounting to annual round trips of well over 600 kilometres. This pattern of seasonal movements is made necessary by two further factors: water and shade. Oryx need to be able to go without drinking water for many months at a time. Sahelian rainfall is limited to a single wet season, during which time rain amounts to only 100–400 millimetres. Not only is rainfall sparse but it is also highly scattered in time and space, factors that modify wildlife distribution to a great degree. Oryx are drawn to areas of new rainfall, giving rise to considerable migrations. Thirsty Oryx will run great risks to get to water and, knowing this, hunters prepare accordingly. As the rainy season develops, oryx follow the rains and new pastures northwards.

On fresh green pasture, Oryx need little or no drinking water, extracting moisture from the plants they eat. As temperatures rise, however, the need for water-rich vegetation increases. If rainfall has been sufficient, succulent plants will have grown along the banks of the Sahelian wadis and in pans and depressions. As a source of moisture, the Wild Melon *Colocythis vulgaris* is of primary importance to the majority of the region's aridland fauna, and wildlife distribution may be modified considerably by its presence or absence.

Along with moisture-rich vegetation, shade is also an important modifying factor in Oryx distribution. Aridland wildlife in general needs good shade during the hot season if it is to conserve body water. Once again, the wooded wadis and inter-dunal depressions of the Sahel provide an essential resource.

Under favourable conditions, it would appear that the Oryx can breed continuously, females becoming receptive a few days after parturition. Gestation is approximately 8½ months and, as a rule, a single calf is produced. Observations made in Chad (Newby, 1978) revealed a reproductive periodicity of about nine months over several consecutive years. During calving periods, young animals made up 12–15% of herds observed. During drought years, calving is disrupted and tends to be restricted to the period immediately following the rains, a situation similar to that observed in antelopes and gazelles living under the harsher climate of the Sahara. During years of severe drought, calf mortality is high and newborn Oryx have been found abandoned (Newby, 1982).

In days gone by, Oryx had to contend with a fair number of large predators—Cheetah *Acinonyx jubatus*, Striped and Spotted Hyaena *Hyaena hyaena* and *Crocuta crocuta*, Wild Dog *Lycaon pictus* and even Lion *Panthera leo*. Owing to systematic persecution, all but the wiliest and hardiest predators have been exterminated from the Sahel.

In spite of their cursory nature, the preceding paragraphs have outlined the Oryx's basic spatial and biological requirements; requirements that, as we shall see, have been severely compromised during the last few decades.

Oryx during the Historical Period

If Meigs's map can be used as an indication of potential Oryx habitat, it is clear that Oryx population north of the Sahara would find themselves geographically more constrained than those south of it. To the east, the Nile is an effective barrier and there is, as yet, no evidence of Scimitar-horned Oryx ever occurring beyond it (Koch, 1970). To the west, the Sahara runs into the Atlantic. Only to the south would the Oryx find themselves unencumbered by physical barriers, and it was here that, until very recently, they lived in large numbers.

In spite of the physical constraints, however, there is ample evidence of Oryx existing north of the Sahara. That they lived in Ancient Egypt is well documented on numerous bas-reliefs and frescoes, especially those associated with the 4th, 5th and 6th Dynasties (4,980–4,475 BP). Funeral inscriptions indicate that both Arabian and Scimitar-horned Oryx were considered valuable property. The tomb of a certain Sabu of Sakkarah, a 6th Dynasty noble, shows that he possessed among his herds 1,308 Oryx. A fresco from the tomb of Khnumhotep, dating from about 3,000 BP, shows Nubian slaves tending a herd of Scimitar-horned Oryx (Janson, 1963). Wilson (1951) refers to the Upper Nile province of Hiracropolis, the hieroglyph of which was the Scimitar-horned Oryx. The last Oryx in Egypt were recorded during the 1850s (Flower, 1932).

Along the North African hinterland, wildlife, although apparently common, found itself not only constrained by the Sahara and the Mediterranean littoral, but also by contact with the successive waves of human occupation that have characterised the region's history. Both Heradotus (484–428 BC) and Strabo (60 BC–?) described the area well, documenting not only the fearsome desert but also the wealth and variety of the wildlife.

Desertification and land degradation apart, man's influence on North Africa's wildlife reached unprecedented levels with the arrival of the Romans after the fall of Carthage in 194 BC. The export of wild beasts from Africa Proconsularis to the circuses was second in importance only to the export of olive oil for the lamps of Rome (Hufnagl, 1972). The Roman craze for *venationes*, or mock hunts, was insatiable and proved a major factor in the extermination of the large mammals of North Africa. Five thousand wild animals were killed at the opening of the Colosseum in 80 AD. On another occasion, Trajan and his gladiators and *bestiarii* slew 2,246 large animals in a single day. The 'splendours' of nature and the circuses were depicted in many exquisite mosaics in which both Addax and Oryx are well represented.

Whilst unable to match the Romans' propensity for wildlife destruction, the following Vandal, Byzantine, Arab, Berber and Turkish occupations must have levied their toll on wildlife and habitat alike. European colonisation and the spread of firearms carried the slaughter into the interior and led to the extinction of

Table 15.1: Extinction dates for Scimitar-horned Oryx within their range states

Algeria	1960s[a]	Grenot, 1974
Burkina Faso	1950s	Roure, 1968
Chad	Extant	Thomassey, pers. comm.
Egypt	1850s	Flower, 1932
Libya	1940s	Hufnagl, 1972
Mali	1981	Lamarche, pers. comm.
Mauritania	1960s	Trotignon, 1975
Morocco	1930s	Cabrera, 1932
Niger	1983?	Newby, *in litt.*
Senegal	1850s	Dupuy, pers. comm.
Sudan	1978	Newby, 1982
Tunisia	1906	Lavauden, 1924
W Sahara	1963	Valverde, 1968

Note: a. At the time this paper was being written, an unconfirmed report was received (de Smet, pers. comm.) of two Oryx found dead to the south of Djanet (SW Algeria) earlier this year.

many Addax and Oryx populations by the beginning of the present century. Table 15.1 tabulates the known extinction dates of Oryx in their range states.

South of the Sahara, the Oryx by no means escaped the ravages of man, but, with vast and inaccessible areas at their disposal, they weathered the storm until more recent times.

The Last 30 Years

A regionally common species 30 years ago, Scimitar-horned Oryx populations have plummeted and today the species is on the verge of extinction in the wild. During the 1950s, several territories under French colonial rule benefited from the establishment of protected areas. Some of these harboured aridland fauna, including Scimitar-horned Oryx. An appraisal of the conservation status of the Addax and Oryx by Gillet (1969), whilst raising serious concern, indicated several locally important populations. Figure 15.2 is reproduced from Gillet's paper and shows the Oryx still with

Figure 15.2: Distribution of Scimitar-horned Oryx during the 1960s (after Gillet, 1969)

a reasonably widespread Sahelian distribution. Concerned by further declines in the numbers of all aridland species, the World Wildlife Fund (WWF), the International Union for Conservation of Nature (IUCN) and the United Nations Environment Programme (UNEP) launched a general survey of the Sahelo-Saharan region in 1974. The survey's results overwhelmingly confirmed that many species were either extinct locally or threatened with extinction. Addax and Oryx populations were becoming increasingly isolated. Figure 15.3 shows Oryx distribution during the 1970s and is based

154

Figure 15.3: Distribution of Scimitar-horned Oryx during the 1970s

on the WWF/IUCN/UNEP findings, together with further information collected by the author ior the latter part of the decade.

By the end of the 1970s, educated guesses put the world
Scimitar-horned Oryx population at around the 6,000 mark. The
work of a number of authors (Lamprey, 1975; Trotignon, 1975;
Gritzner, 1981; Newby, 1982) shows that the decline in Oryx
numbers, and those of aridland wildlife populations in general, is
impossible to attribute to a single cause. The reasons are multiple
and have by and large acted in concert.

Drought and Desertification

Climatic change has been a major factor in influencing Oryx distribution and survival. The generally arid conditions that began 3,000 to 4,000 years ago continue, and their cumulative long-term effects have led to desertification and habitat change along the sub-arid fringes of an expanding Sahara. Within recent decades, this trend has been punctuated by a number of particularly severe droughts—in the 1940s, 1968–73, 1976–80 and 1983–84 (National Research Council, 1983). As a result, large areas of Sahelian and Saharan pasture have disappeared. Lack of rainfall has failed to provoke the growth of the rich, ephemeral desert pastures upon which aridland ungulates depend for wet-and-cool-season grazing and from which they can lay down adequate reserves to endure the rigours of the waterless, hot-season months. Drought has killed back even the most resilient perennial grasses and shrubs, plants that are staple to the ungulates' hot-season diet. Trees have been especially hard hit and the regeneration of new ones curtailed or reduced to spasmodic periods of growth interrupted by long periods of quiescence. Once an important source of dry-season nutrition and shade, dead *Acacia* trees litter the Sahel. Meagre rainfall has severely reduced the flow of wadis and the inundation of the floodplains and pans, so necessary for the growth of the water-rich plants vital to the hot-season survival of aridland wildlife.

The effect of drought and desertification on aridland wildlife in general, and on the Oryx and Addax in particular, has been catastrophic: fewer and smaller winter pastures, rarefaction of dry-season grazing, loss of shade and depletion of vital sources of organic water. By the hot season, Oryx and Addax are severely weakened, some die of hunger, others of thirst or disease. Reproduction is disrupted or curtailed entirely, calves are aborted or abandoned at birth. In the search for grazing, the wildlife is driven south prematurely and onto land occupied by herders or farmers on the northern edge of the agricultural zone.

Habitat Loss Due to Man

Whilst large tracts of oryx habitat have been lost to desertification, an equally large amount is being withheld from them by man. Over the past few decades, the marginal aridlands of the Sahel have come under a great deal of human pressure. Large areas of once virgin or seasonally used land are now permanently occupied or have been heavily degraded by poor land-use practices. In the past, permanent use of sub-Saharan grasslands was not only difficult, since water resources were largely ephemeral, but also constrained by the tribal warfare that dissuaded the establishment or activities of isolated groups of people. With the subjugation of the powerful nomadic tribes during the early colonial period, large areas of no-man's-land, previously inhabited by wildlife, became available to man. Farmers were free to extend their fields, their ranks swelled by the enfranchisement of large numbers of slaves and serfs. Encouraged by better-than-average rainfall during the 1950s and early 1960s, farmers were perhaps for the first time able to extend their activities into the northern Sahel.

Pastoralism, too, has seen many radical changes during the past 30 years. Inter-tribal warfare apart, nomads were formerly obliged to quit the waterless Sahelian and sub-desert pastures when the shallow wells and pans ran dry. By the hot season, the nomads had moved south with their herds to areas of permanent water, leaving behind them almost limitless areas of virtually unexploited grazing. Wildlife, free from the need to drink, moved into these areas.

With independence in the early 1960s, the new Sahelian states began to benefit from international aid programmes, foremost of which was the development of the waterless pastoral lands. Boreholes were sunk, deep wells cemented and pumping stations installed, and for a short time nomads had access to rich, new pastoral resources. What the developers failed to foresee, however, was the gross over-grazing that was to take place, the subsequent erosion and the desertification. Neither did they take into account the droughts of the late 1960s and 1970s. With changed herding patterns and increased livestock numbers, millions of head of cattle died for want of food, not water.

Faced by human presence, burgeoning livestock numbers and rapidly increasing over-grazing, Oryx found themselves ousted onto marginal lands and into an uncomfortable co-existence with man and his herds.

Hunting

Oryx have been hunted for millenia, a fact portrayed in innumerable prehistoric engravings and paintings. The arrival in Africa of

157

the Horse (c. 1,600 BC) and Dromedary (c. 200 AD) must have revolutionised the hunt in much the same way as desert-going vehicles have done during the 20th century.

Until very recently, not only were Oryx an important source of meat for local consumption, but they also supplied a prestigious and perhaps lucrative trade in leather products. Nomads still recognise Oryx hide as being of superior quality, suitable for all manner of goods—ropes, harnessing, storage sacks, etc. The Berber peoples prized the hide from the Oryx's neck and shoulders for making the shields with which they went into battle with spear and broadsword. Harper (1945) mentions that a King of Rio de Oro sent a gift of a thousand such shields to a contemporary during the Middle Ages. Further mention of the trade in Oryx hide is made by Leo Africanus, writing during the 16th century. Six hundred skins were sent from the 'land of the Negroes' by caravan to Fez. According to the caravan's 'bill of lading', each skin was worth eight ducates, roughly half the price of a male slave! In more recent times, Nachtigal (1879) describes the use of Oryx hide for saddlery, cords and even for the shoeing of horses.

Oryx-hunting was the major activity of a number of Sahelo-Saharan tribes. Much of the culture and livelihood of groups such as the Nedmadi of Mali and Mauritania, the Aza and Mahalbi of Niger, and the Haddat of Chad and Sudan came from the hunt. With their traditional arms—spears, bows, throwing sticks, nets and dogs—these hunters were extremely effective but could hardly have had a significant effect on overall wildlife populations, considering the logistic problems of moving and hunting in such an arid environment.

With the later colonisation and development of the sub-arid pastoral and agricultural lands, hunters found themselves closer to their prey and with access to new sources of permanent water. As a result, they began to have a much greater impact on wildlife numbers. Man's dominance of the aridlands has been further enhanced by the development of reliable four-wheel-drive vehicles. As an essential tool for all desert-based mining, exploration and construction projects, the desert-going vehicle has facilitated the almost universally practised hunting activities that accompany these operations. There is little need of a gun when one can just as easily run the animal to its death. For their part, too, the authorised bearers of arms consistently abuse their authority, interpreting it as a licence to kill with impunity. Guerrilla and open warfare have also levied a heavy toll on wildlife numbers. Tourists, avid for adventure and snapshots, will course after Oryx and Addax, finally leaving them to die of heat exhaustion. Virtually all photographs of oryx or Addax in the wild portray an animal in full gallop with froth-flecked mouth and dangling tongue. That conservation journals persist in using this sort of picture is disgraceful.

Whilst it would be easy to expand upon any one of the aforementioned topics, suffice it to say that the decline in Oryx numbers over the past few decades cannot be attributed to any single cause, but is the result of a number of contributing factors embraced by habitat loss and over-exploitation. Given its precise ecological requirements, the Oryx has been found, like so many other species, to be incompatible with man and his activities and prone to the natural environmental changes that have, throughout the earth's history, been responsible for the rarefaction of species and ultimately their extinction.

The Current Situation

In all probability, Chad is today the only country harbouring a viable, wild population of Scimitar-horned Oryx. The Addax, although more widespread, exists in tiny and ever-dwindling herds isolated by vast expanses of desert. In Niger, the last reliable reports of Scimitar-horned Oryx date back to 1983, when a herd of four was spotted between the Air mountains and Termit, a small massif lying to the east. Up until 1982, the odd animal was seen on the edge of the Air itself—I personally saw four in 1980—but since then nothing has been seen. In 1984, Niger suffered its worst single drought year in living memory and it is likely that any Oryx still alive would have been driven south to certain death at the hands of hunters. In spite of this, a few nomads believe that Oryx may still exist in the Termit area. An expedition mounted in 1986 found no sign, but it is just possible that a few Oryx remain.

Despite the long years of civil war in Chad, the latest reports (Thomassey, pers. comm.) are encouraging and affirm the continued presence of Oryx in their former stronghold, the Ouadi Rime-Ouadi Achim Faunal Reserve (77,950 km^2). For many years this reserve harboured the majority of the world's Scimitar-horned Oryx, an estimated 5,000–6,000 in 1978. The Government of Chad is keen to retake control of the reserve and, with international assistance, hopes to mount a survey of the area in 1988. If the

Figure 15.4: Distribution of Scimitar-horned Oryx during the 1980s. 'x' indicates isolated observations

current peace in Chad holds, there is every chance of rehabilitating the reserve and saving a viable population of wild Oryx.

Figure 15.4 shows the distribution of known Oryx sightings for the first part of this decade. In the absence of any real data, an estimate of Oryx numbers must, at best, be limited to the very low hundreds.

Rehabilitation of Oryx in the Wild

Within the past few years, only Chad and Niger have harboured viable populations of Scimitar-horned Oryx. In both countries, the creation or rehabilitation of protected areas large enough to encompass the annual movements of the Oryx is essential. The reserves will necessarily be vast and require sizeable long-term funding to manage them correctly. At the present time, Niger is establishing a 77,360-km^2 reserve centred on the Air mountains and Eastern Tenere Desert. Although the area has been visited by Oryx in recent times, it is marginal to their preferred sub-Saharan range. The reserve was designed principally to accommodate Addax and other species inhabiting the more clement mountain and valley habitats of the Air itself—Dorcas and Dama Gazelles *Gazella dorcas* and *G. dama*, Ostrich, Cheetah and Barbary Sheep. Niger would seriously like to see a second aridland reserve established around Termit to protect the area's Sahelo-Saharan habitats and faunal resources. Lessons drawn from the Air/Tenere experience indicate that this will be possible only if the Governmment can obtain long-term technical and financial assistance. In terms of aridland conservation, a reserve at Termit is an extremely high priority since the region still harbours fair numbers of gazelle, a healthy population of Cheetah, Barbary Sheep and perhaps Niger's last Oryx. The conservation status of all these species has deteriorated badly and will surely worsen rapidly if nothing is done. A third Niger reserve, that of Gadabedgi (7,600 km^2), was created in 1955 for the protection of Oryx and other aridland species. The reserve has never had any real protection and is a classic example of the 'paper' protected area. Wildlife has virtually disappeared, but the habitat is still in good condition. With the help of the Dutch Government, Niger hopes to manage the reserve's forestry and pastoral resources and there is certainly potential for developing a wildlife-rehabilitation programme.

In Chad, it is clear that the conservation of whatever Oryx may remain is inextricably related to the rehabilitation of the Ouadi Rime-Ouadi Achim Reserve. This can only be brought about with peace and substantial external funding.

Oryx Re-introduction and Captive Breeding

By comparison with the Arabian Oryx in the early 1960s, the Scimitar-horned Oryx would seem to have a considerable advantage. Large numbers of Scimitar-horned Oryx have been bred in captivity and are held in a wide range of collections. Studbooks have been kept and, with the changes in zoo philosophy, many establishments see re-introduction as the principal objective of their endangered species captive-breeding programmes. Furthermore, any Scimitar-horned Oryx re-introduction scheme would benefit enormously from the Omani and Jordanian experiences and from the recent work with Scimitar-horned Oryx in Tunisia.

In my opinion, captive-bred Scimitar-horned Oryx should be re-introduced into the Sahel, even though some may still survive in the wild. Apart from the threats that these survivors face, their reproductive viability is far from certain. The genetics of the zoo-bred stock has also raised some doubt since a great number of captive-bred animals originate from a limited stock of Oryx captured mostly in Chad. A mixing of wild and captive stock may be necessary to improve bloodlines.

Whilst it is absolutely essential that Sahelian governments be able to guarantee the safety of re-introduced herds, the major constraint on re-introduction taking place is the lack of funds with which to build, man and maintain the re-introduction sites and captive-breeding facilities. Sahelian governments would have to apply for external funding, something few donors would be willing to give in view of the nature of the operation and the long-term commitment required. Nonetheless, recent talks with a major donor have revealed a certain amount of interest and further contacts are planned. The establishment of a regional Sahelian captive-breeding centre would seem appropriate, and a number of zoos have already stated their willingness to provide Oryx (Zoological Society of London, Marwell, Hannover, Rotterdam, etc.). The Sahelian centre could accommodate not only Addax and Oryx, but also other endangered aridland species such as Dama Gazelle and West African Ostrich. The centre's establishment would create a great deal of pride and interest, and motivate and encourage the governments to take the kind of measures necessary to ensure the protection of any released animals. Whilst it is unlikely that the Sahelian governments will be able to match the financial and human resources afforded the Arabian Oryx work by the Omanis and Jordanians, there is a genuine regret for the passing of wildlife in the Sahel and a strong desire to see it rehabilitated.

Action Plan for the Conservation and Rehabilitation of the Scimitar-horned Oryx

The following programme would seem essential if the Scimitar-horned Oryx is to be saved from extinction in the wild and subsequently rehabilitated.

Conservation of Wild Populations

1. A survey of the Ouadi Rime Reserve in Chad to assess the conservation status of remaining herds.

2. Rehabilitation of the Ouadi Rime Reserve with the creation of a special Scimitar-horned Oryx conservation unit.

3. A survey of the Termit region of Niger.

4. Establishment of a protected area centred on Termit.

5. Surveys of any other areas likely to harbour Oryx (e.g. eastern Mali, southwest Algeria, western Sudan).

Re-introduction

1. Establishment of a regional Sahelian captive-breeding centre for aridland wildlife.

2. Re-introduction of Scimitar-horned Oryx herds into appropriate protected areas in the Sahelo-Saharan region.

It is clear that very few of these activities can take place without considerable financial and technical assistance. The whole programme could take many years to realise, but, if we consider the conservation of aridland wildlife a priority, there are no short cuts. Funds and time apart, the realisation of such a programme will ultimately depend on the Sahelian governments' willingness to come to terms with a number of problems—lack of adequate wildlife laws, lack of qualified manpower, poor protected-area management, bad land-use planning etc. Whatever direct action conservation bodies can take, it must be accompanied by activities to bolster the governments' ability and capacity to undertake serious wildlife conservation and management commitments.

163

Conclusions

Having heard the preceding dismal story, many people will wonder whether Scimitar-horned Oryx conservation is even worth bothering with. The cards certainly seem to be stacked against aridland wildlife ever regaining any semblance of former numbers. With large areas of habitat lost to desertification and human activities, and the constant threat of hunting and harassment, prospects are very grim indeed.

In spite of this, I personally feel that we should redouble our efforts and re-introduce Oryx into the Sahel. Loss is a powerful stimulus and in many ways would sadly seem necessary before the true value of something can be appreciated. Sentimentality has been the driving force of the conservation movement for years, and I am personally convinced that the preservation of many species will ultimately depend on the cutural, spiritual and aesthetic values people associate with them, rather than on any economic or ecological arguments that may be forwarded in their favour. Having said this, I am not ignoring the ecological facts of life. The environmental catastrophe that the Sahel is going through is also a signal lesson in ecological principles and one that has been vividly illustrated by the mistakes made in trying to 'develop' without due respect for environmental and ecological parameters. There is today a great deal more awareness of the need to maintain ecological stability, lest the land-based economies of the Sahelian states collapse even further under the pressure of increasing populations, bad land use and soaring abuse of natural resources. Sahelians are becoming increasingly aware of the value of protected areas in maintaining ecological equilibria, biological diversity and basic life-support systems. The role of wildlife as natural agents of land maintenance and their capacity to use habitats unsuited to man's land-use practices, have not escaped their attention either. Major donors are at last listening more objectively to ecologists and conservationists and organisations such as the World Bank should be applauded for their efforts in trying to integrate ecological policy guidelines into their development programmes. The 'greening' of the donor agencies will be as much a factor in the environmental rehabilitation of the Sahel as the genuine desire of the Sahelians themselves to see this happen.

It is foolish to imagine that we can turn the clocks back to the good old days when Oryx roamed a pristine Sahel. Conservation philosophy must change, or forever fight a losing battle against the odds. Species conservation is destined to fail unless integrated with broader land-use strategies. Like it or not, the world's population is growing and the Sahelian states are themselves fighting for survival. For wildlife conservation to be relegated to the bottom of the priorities list is hardly surprising.

In spite of the threats facing Oryx and other aridland species, there is room for them and their survival could be assured if people got together to make this happen. This symposium is a unique forum for launching such a strategy. If we walk away from here without having decided on a concerted effort to save the oryx, we shall have dealt its chances of survival the severest of blows—the last one.

References

Brouin, G. (1950) Notes sur les ongules du Cercle d'Agadez et leur chasse. In *Contribution à l'Etude de l'Air*. Mem. IFAN 10: 425–55.

Cabrera, A. (1932) Los mamiferos de Marruecos Trabajos. *Mus. Cienc. Nat.* Ser. Zool. 57, Madrid.

Flower, S.S. (1932) Notes on the recent mammals of Egypt, with a list of the species recorded from the Kingdom. *Proc. Zool. Soc. Lond.*: pp. 369–450.

Gillet, H. (1964) Pâturages et faune sauvage dans le Nord Tchad. *Journal d'Agric. Tropic. et de Bot. Appliquée XI*: 155–76.

Gillet, H. (1965) L'oryx algazelle et l'addax au Tchad. *La Terre et la Vie 3*: 257–72.

Gillet, H. (1969) L'oryx algazelle et l'addax. Distribution géographique. Chances de survie. *C.R. Biogéogr. 405*: 177–89.

Grenot, C. (1974) Ecologie appliquée à la conservation et à l'élevage des ongules sauvages au Sahara Algérien. *CNRS*, Paris.

Gritzner, J. (1981) *Environmental Degradation in Mauritania*. National Research Council, Washington D.C.

Harper, F. (1945) Extinct and vanishing mammals of the Old World. *Spec. Publ. Amer. Comm. Int. Wild Life Prot.* 12.

Hufnagl, E. (1972) *Libyan Mammals*. Oleander Press, Cambridge.

Janson, H. (1963) *History of Art*. Prentice Hall Inc., Englewood Cliffs, NJ.

Koch, D. (1970) Zur Verbreitung der Mendesantilope, *Addax nasomaculatus* (De Blainville 1916), und des Spiessbockes, *Oryx gazella* (Linne 1758) im Nilgebiet. Ein Beitrag zur Zoogeographie Nordafrikas. *Saugertierk. mitt. 18* (1): 25–37.

Lamprey, H. (1975) Report on the desert encroachment reconnaissance in Northern Sudan. Report to IUCN/UNEP.

Lavauden L. (1924) *La Chasse et la Faune Cynégétique en Tunisie*. Tunis.

Malbrant, R. (1953) *Faune de Centre Africain Français*. Paris.

Maley, R. (1981) *Etudes Palynologiques dans le Bassin du Tchad et Paléoclimatologie de l'Afrique Nord-Tropicale de 30,000 Ans à l'Epoque Actuelle*. Trav. Docum. 129, ORSTOM, Paris.

Mauny, R. (1957) Repartition de la grande faune éthiopienne du Nord-Ouest Africain du Paléolithique à nos jours. *Proc. 3rd Pan-Afr. Cong. Prehist.* Livingstone 1955, 102–5.

McBurney, C. (1960) *The Stone Age of Northern Africa*. Pelican, London.

Meigs, P. (1953) World distribution of arid and semi-arid holoclimates. UNESCO, *Progr. zone aride*, I.

Myers, N. (1979) *The Sinking Ark*. Pergamon Press, London.

Nachtigal, G. (1879) *Sahara und Sudan*. Berlin.

National Research Council (1983) *Environmental Change in the West African Sahel*. National Academy Press, Washington D.C.

Newby, J. (1975) The Addax and Scimitar-horned Oryx in Chad and Niger. Report to IUCN/WWF/UNEP.

Newby, J. (1978) The ecological resources of the Ouadi Rime-Ouadi Achim Faunal Reserve, Chad. Report to FAO.

Newby, J. (1981) Desert antelopes in retreat. *World Wildlife News*, summer 1981: pp. 14–18.

Newby, J. (1982) Action plan for the Sahelo-Saharan fauna of Africa. Report to IUCN/WWF, Gland, Switzerland.

Nicholson, S. (1982) *The Sahel: A Climatic Perspective*. Club du Sahel, Paris.

Petit-Maire, N. (1984) Le Sahara, de la steppe au desert. *La Recherche 160*: 1372–82.

Rognon, P. (1976) Oscillations climatiques au Sahara depuis 40,000 ans. *Rev. Geogr. Phys. Geol. dyn. 18* (2).

Roure, G. (1968) *Animaux Sauvages de Haute-Volta et des Pays Voisins*. FAP/Direction des Eaux et Forêts, Haute-Volta.

Trotignon, J. (1975) Le status et la conservation de l'Addax et l'Oryx et de la faune associée en Mauritanie. Report to IUCN/WWF/UNEP.

Valverde, J. (1968) Ecological bases for fauna conservation in Western Sahara. *Proc. IBP/CT Tech. Meeting Cons. Nat.* Hammamet, Tunisia.

Wilson, J. (1951) *The Burden of Eygpt*. Univ. Chicago Press, Chicago.

16. Discussion

Panel: *Dr Mark Stanley Price, Mr John Newby*
and Mr David Jones

David Jones: Yesterday, we dealt with the history of 'Operation Oryx' and today we have discussed our present situation, our increasing knowledge of the Arabian Oryx and some related species with related problems. Indeed, the situation is identical for most of the species discussed today. I would like now to consider the future of the Arabian Oryx and then also of the Scimitar-horned Oryx and Addax. But first I would like to open the floor to questions.

Paul Munton: One of the elements in the success of the Oryx project in Oman has been the help of the Harasis. How do you motivate local people?

Ralph Daly: Without the support of the local people, our project in Oman would have come to nothing at all. The situation was that we had the interest of the Sultan, the right conditions, and a tribe that was as angry as anybody at the removal of their last Oryx. I am not trying to say that they had never shot or eaten an Oryx in the past—they had—but they had done it in such a way that the offtake was minimal and was not what eventually drove the Oryx out of the area altogether.

How did we do it? Individual discussions with bedu tribesmen made it clear that the project would have definite benefits for them—return of a part of their cultural heritage and employment. Almost as soon as we started, we had a constant stream of other people who also wanted Oryx projects. Now, with the conservation programme covering the whole country, there is a great emphasis placed on the need to employ and to have spin-off benefits for the people of the regions which are going to be protected. I think it is a matter of explanation of what it is you are

167

trying to do and a determination to provide not only salaries, but also motivation, something which keeps them interested and active in their own areas rather than drifting away to seek employment in the towns, especially something which involves them in an area in which they themselves are expert.

David Jones: The problem of resources, of setting up an infrastructure, is one which must be dealt with for any re-introduction project. What are your comments, John [Newby]?

John Newby: There are certain similarities between the North African situation and the Omani one. In Niger, for example, the Tuareg nomads, within whose range the Oryx and Addax recently existed, and, in the case of the Addax, still does exist, were not the ones responsible for the decimation of the herds and they regret the loss of these animals very much. So *a priori* they are keen to see these animals brought back, but what they are actually able to do is often limited by what the Administration lets them do. Obviously, we have not got an enlightened ruler in the same way as Oman has benefited from the enlightenment of the Sultan. This is a big constraint on getting anything done, but the people themselves want the animals brought back for no other reason than that the animals mean something to them, not because of the spin-off benefits. With regard to funding, the Sahelian countries know they have absolutely no means of doing this sort of thing themselves. Wildlife conservation is not a priority and that is totally understandable. This means looking for outside funding. I am also convinced that, if such funding were obtained and a project started up, it would immediately create the kind of interest which is necessary to motivate the governments not only to carry on with the work that is being done, but also to extend it to other conservation problems such as the protection of re-introduced animals or to encourage them to look after what they have got. I think the establishment of an Oryx project would have a catalytic effect of prompting the development of a new attitude to conservation.

Mark Stanley Price: There are differences between Sahelian Africa and Arabia, but there is no doubt that the Oryx project in Oman probably was the stimulus for a lot of interest on a regional basis in Oryx conservation and re-introduction. It has promoted a general interest in environmental conservation and I would also say that, at a local level in central Oman, the spin-off effects of employing 17 rangers to look after the Oryx actually consolidated a very large area. A population of 5,000 to 8,000 Gazelle were fully protected over 3,000 square kilometres at no extra add-on costs because the hearts-and-minds effect of working with and protecting the Oryx probably guaranteed total protection of the Gazelle more effectively than if you had mounted a special force and cruised around in motor cars, so I agree entirely with John's catalytic effect.

David Jones: It is the principle of having a keynote species which has worked well in other areas—the Tiger in India, for example. Perhaps it is worth clarifying in an effort to get things moving we are now examining the possibility of a Scimitar-horned Oryx re-introduction project in Niger which would involve a number of institutions.

Paul Gill (Edinburgh Zoo): In her talk this afternoon, Georgina Mace made the point that, to maintain genetic diversity in sufficiently large populations captured for subsequent re-introduction, it might be better to delay breeding up to the maximum generation time where this is known. Thus, while aiming to increase the size and founder representation of the population, am I correct in thinking that we should only aim to produce a large number of F1 calves? Could we separate breeding males, especially in less arid-adapted species which Tim spoke of, or should we not be encouraging the development of a truly reversible harmless contraceptive for this purpose?

David Jones: Georgina, clearly, given your figures about the reproductive rates, the number of spaces in Noah's Zoo Ark are going to be filled up pretty quickly with both Scimitar-horned and Arabian Oryx, probably within the next decade or so. We will have too many animals so we have to slow reproduction down and we have to control which animals we are using.

Georgina Mace: Yes, it is a very complicated issue. The extreme argument and the extreme conclusion of that point is that the very best way you can extend generation length is to have only one generation. The effective way to do that is to store gametes and embryos, what has been talked about as the frozen zoo, and there

169

are all kinds of issues which arise from that, which I will not discuss here. Extending generation length is an effective way of slowing down the rate of loss of genetic variation, but it clearly conflicts with other aims of a captive-breeding programme such as another one I emphasised very strongly which is getting the captive population to carrying capacity very quickly. I think the answer is that in the early stages of a captive-breeding programme, when one actually has very few animals, you need to breed them quickly and get them up to that capacity. Thereafter, and because you do then confront these problems of limited resources and competing demands upon these resources, the population needs to be managed for longer generation lengths at a reasonable carrying capacity that is a good compromise between loss of diversity and the constraints of resources. This is really the sort of issue which has to be resolved on the basis of species groups because Scimitar-horned Oryx and Arabian Oryx will to some extent be competing for the same resources and it will be necessary to make some quite hard decisions in that particular area.

David Jones: It might be worth saying that our experts in the Nuffield Laboratories at the Institute of Zoology are now fairly confident that they can store antelope semen for more or less infinity. Five years ago this was just not possible and there was a lot of scepticism that artificial insemination using frozen semen would not be a feasible prospect within a decade. However, there have been some major advances in that field within the last two or three years. The hope is that we will be able to get over the problem of having to keep a lot of male animals which are expensive and require a great deal of space. Within the next couple of years it should be possible to keep and use genetic material much more selectively, bearing in mind the problems of actual insemination and the practicalities of handling animals.

Peter Jewell: I would like to follow that point up. Remembering what Georgina Mace said about the different selective forces at work on a captive group and once they are released into the wild, and the high mortality which occurs in the wild, is there a possibility of bringing back for breeding purposes a few of the males which have survived in the wild after release and to use them specifically because they have successfully re-adapted?

Discussion

David Jones: The great difficulty would be quarantine regulations. The countries we are dealing with have a large range of endemic diseases. Import regulations in the UK and Europe are stringent, and the USA is even tougher, so it is a problem. Certainly, with Scimitar-horned Oryx in particular, we would like to introduce some wild genes into the captive population because, as said earlier, most of those in captivity are descended from a group of 41 caught in western Chad in 1966. The problem, apart from actually locating suitable wild animals, is quarantine. Probably this could be overcome, as it was with the Arabian Oryx which was quarantined through several different places. The same difficulty would occur with importing captive-bred animals that have been put back into the wild; it would be very hard to get back Tunisian Scimitar-horned Oryx, for example.

Mark Stanley Price: The quarantine aspect does make things difficult. If one wants to get genes back from the wild, you would have to do it with sperm which would get over the veterinary problem. It would also have the advantage that you could leave the owner of the sperm in the wild. When a population goes extinct, a great body of social knowledge and experience is lost forever. This is one implication of removing the last animals from the wild; there may be sound genetic reasons, but the social considerations are also important. The corollary is that, when one puts an animal back into the wild, one has to look after it until a body of knowledge is re-evolved. I would therefore argue that some animals, particularly dominant males, may be very important in the wild for more than just genetic reasons. It will depend on the social organisation of the animals and so on, but I do not think one should regard the removal from the wild of re-introduced captive-bred animals as a light decision.

Colin Groves: You said that the sex ratio overall is 50:50, but there was the implication in some of the talks that some of the bloodlines do show a tendency to throw off male or female calves. Is this so, or is there some identifiable environmental factor that tends to modify the sex ratio? Can it be artificially manipulated?

Georgina Mace: Overall, the sex ratio is more or less 50:50. What does seem to happen is that there will be a run of males within certain groups, not necessarily within lineages or particular animals. The exception was the run of males in Oman where one bull was siring all the calves. This group phenomenon may be the result of some process like selective abortion of females in newly formed herds. However, there is no statistically significant effect overall of one sex dominating; it is a more anecdotal observation that within newly established herds there is a run of males for whatever reason we do not as yet understand.

David Jones: In a discussion of a few weeks ago on the storage of sperm, the question of whether x and y chromosomes could be separated out was also considered. There are procedures whereby they can be recognised but what we need now if it is to be morally acceptable, is a means of separating them mechanically.

Michael Brambell: I think on this question of sex ratios we ought not to discuss the runs of males quite so lightly, because the net 50:50 we are now getting I think is the result of two, perhaps three, different processes. There seems to be very good evidence in zoos that, where one has small breeding groups, one gets runs of males. It seems to me that the spates of males have happened where females have been singly with males and, where there has been more than one female together, the tendency has been for female offspring. As soon as the group starts building up, the ratio goes to 50:50.

David Jones: Mark, you have said the Jidda' could hold 200 animals. How many would you reckon could be handled ideally in Oman and how many do you want from the captive population? In other words, when do we stop?

Mark Stanley Price: A minimum effective breeding population of 200 with an animal like the Oryx would mean an actual population of 400 to 500 individuals at least. The test is whether the predictions from the models are actually correct. I am certain that a number of large animals survived and did very well with small populations. The point of how long one must introduce immigrants into the population depends on how much one is prepared to let a purely natural rate of increase take one up to a population level which is independent and viable, and subject to all the natural processes of mortality without adverse effects. I would not like to say categorically how long this might be, but I would think that, with an annual input of ten animals which start to breed immediately, perhaps another five years.

David Jones: Is it true to say that within Arabia there are actually very few places where one could practically re-introduce Oryx?

Mark Stanley Price: The Jiddat-al-Harasis is a distinct geological unit and, if one assumes that the carrying capacity is approximately one Oryx per 30 square kilometres, that does work out at a very convenient 200 Oryx in that ecological area. But there are much bigger areas beyond, which were certainly once used by the Oryx either seasonally or sporadically. Because it is the desert and because it is erratic and unpredictable, it is very hard to put finite figures on how big the population can actually be. I think one has to turn it around and say how many must we have in order to feel secure about them and how big an area do they have to occupy, or know, to survive.

David Jones: So, for the foreseeable future and looking beyond Oman's borders, you are saying that we can soak up all the animals generated by captive breeding.

Mark Stanley Price: I think so, yes, especially as the numbers increase in the wild and the rarity of the animals decreases and we can therefore afford to take risks. For example, we have always thought in terms of releasing animals only from Yalooni but now, with solar fencing and the Oryx's inability to jump anyway, we could think of setting up temporary release sites elsewhere. By doing this, we could have low-cost/relatively high-risk mini-release programmes in all sorts of places.

David Jones: So really it will come down to the attitude of the local people and not the scale of available resources.

Mark Stanley Price: Certainly for the foreseeable future, if there are regular batches of animals coming into Oman, say one a year, and if the release process is established and understood, the time scale could be shortened for putting the Oryx in the wild and the project could go on at Yalooni without increasing staff.

Discussion

David Jones: John [Newby], given that the captive population of Scimitar-horned Oryx will almost certainly rise above 2,000 this year and that there are now plenty of animals available, what are your views about setting up a similar project in North Africa?

John Newby: I think that we have to start out in the Sahel exactly the way we did in Oman. Just think of all the spin-offs the Omani operation has had. It is incredibly high-profile public relations, it has influenced the way people are thinking in the whole Arabian peninsula with regard to conserving wildlife. Unfortunately, the wave created by the Omani and Jordanian operations has yet to reach the Sahel and, even if it did, there is nothing like doing it in your own country to stimulate people's interest. I would agree with what Mark said and I also think we can cut a few corners now because we do have a lot of Scimitar-horned Oryx in captivity. I think we can learn from the Omani experience and modify it slightly so that we can move forward more quickly, but basically it will boil down to local interest, government support and external technical and financial assistance.

17. Wildlife in Arabia: Animals and Attitudes

Jonathan Kingdon

In other circumstances, a recent visitor would not dare to pronounce on the status of wildlife in a vast peninsula that has been peopled by the world's most ancient civilisations. In the case of Arabia, however, new-found public interest in its wildlife and conservation has encountered a vacuum of information about the region's animals and plants. Having been drawn into the vacuum, this traveller's observations, albeit with the bias of a mammal specialist, may help to promote interest in a fascinating fauna.

The first thing to stress about the Arabian peninsula is its size: 3½ million km^2, that is seven times the size of France. Arabia is therefore a sizeable part of the habitable world and currently supports some 30 million people. In spite of its aridity, the entire peninsula is traditionally owned pasture or arable land for over 60 different tribes, many of them nomadic. Its wealth in oil has tended to eclipse awareness of the rich history and natural history of the region.

Another point to stress about Arabian natural history is how little is known about it in the West. Very few travellers from the outside ever visited the interior and, before David Harrison published his splendid work on Arabian mammals (1964–72), English naturalists relied mainly on reports by St John Philby and Major Cheesman from the 1920s and 1930s and Wilfred Thesiger's travels in the 1950s for some picture of animal life in the Arabian interior. To illustrate how little and late is our knowledge, the Arabian Sheep *Ovis vignei arabica* was described scientifically only last year.

There are just over 100 species of mammals in the Arabian peninsula. The larger herbivores are typified by five or six species of gazelle, four species of wild sheep and goats and, of course, the Arabian Oryx. Of special interest are the recently recognised

Queen of Sheba Gazelle *Gazella bilkis* from Yemen, the Red Sea Island isolate, the Farasan Gazelle *Gazella arabica*, and a new recognition that the little Saudi Desert Gazelle *Gazella dorcas saudiya* is probably a full species.

Not surprisingly, a high proportion of Arabian mammals are adapted to great heat and to going without water. Yet not all of Arabia is a desert, and its climate and habitats have been much less degraded in the past. The west and south are mountainous, with steep precipices marking the Rift Wall above the Red Sea. The whole landmass tilts down towards the east except for the ancient Hajjar mountain range which sticks up in the southeastern corner in Oman.

The environments vary greatly in geological structure, soils and vegetation. Vast sand dunes make up the Rub-al-Khali and other sand deserts; there are hard stony plateaux and open dry steppes in the centre. There are salt flats in the east and savanna littorals in the south and west, while the north is dominated by the wide, well-watered Mesopotamian Valley.

Especially interesting features of Arabian natural history are the many indications of past climatic changes. Arabia has been wetter and drier than the present: past rainfall is known by water-rolled rocks and eroded valleys. It has also been hotter and colder. It has had past connections with Africa across the Bab el Mandab and there are numerous African elements in the flora and fauna of this southwestern corner, although, overall, Asiatic and African elements are about equally balanced. Several groups have one species adapted to cold aridity and another species to hot and dry. In every case the cold/dry species is of Asiatic origin and the hot/dry species has African connections. The gerbils *Gerbillus* spp. typify Arabian fauna, with four Saharo-Arabian, four Asiatic species and three Arabian endemics.

Endemics are of special interest, and the Arabian Oryx, Arabian Tahr *Hemitragus jayakari* and several gazelle species currently provide the major focus for conservation efforts in several Arabian states—all are endangered. (It is often forgotten that the Dromedary *Camelus dromedarius* is also an Arabian endemic.) Reasons for the perilous status of these and many other animals and plants differ from species to species and place to place, but four major time scales are involved.

The first time scale involves millions of years. The geographic isolation of Arabia has stranded some organisms that are relatively primitive within their own lineages. The Arabian Tahr, a precursor of the goats, is typical of such relict species. Its rarity is due partly to eclipse elsewhere by more advanced types of Wild Goat *Capra aegagrus*.

The second time scale is probably prehistoric. Decline of wildlife in Mesopotamia began very early. Asiatic Elephants *Elephas maximus* and Rhinos (Rhinocerotidae) disappeared in prehistoric times. The wild ox *Bos* sp. and the Water Buffalo *Bubalus arnee* were eliminated during the rise of ancient civilisations in Mesopotamia, and the development of livestock competing with their relatives has been another factor (especially for wild sheep).

The third phase of wildlife decline was more recent. In 1845, George Wallin described herds of gazelle, Oryx and Ostrich, and numerous Ibex *Capra ibex*, Hyaenas *Hyaena hyaena* and *Crocuta crocuta*, wolves *Canis* sp. and other smaller fauna in northern Arabia. This was just before the English, French and Germans began to compete with one another in the export of literally millions of cheap, mass-produced guns. By the beginning of this century, guns were almost ubiquitous among adult males in many parts of Arabia, and Wild Ass *Equus hemionus*, Lion *Panthera leo*, Cheetah *Acinonyx jubatus*, Oryx and Ostrich had become very rare and their extermination was only a matter of time.

Finally, there is the most recent past and present. The development of motor transport and, most recently, universal mobility (owing to the oil boom) have put the seal on all species that can be pursued and shot from a vehicle. There is some indication that volcanic lava flows and other areas that are inaccessible to traffic are the last strongholds for a few Wild Sheep, gazelles, Ibex and Leopards *Panthera pardus nimr*. The open plains and wadis are now almost empty of animals. What can explain such a thorough extermination of wildlife? There are many factors at work, but the simplest explanation lies in the peculiar vulnerability of animals in an open desert and the effective absence of prohibitions on the killing of animals. Indeed, the opposite has applied. From the earliest times any large herbivore that could be caught was part of the bounty of the desert, a source of meat for the nomads and a source of recreation for their urbanised cousins or their rulers; 2,700-year-old poems describe the joys of the chase.

Hunting in one form or another has always been an intrinsic part of their youthful experience for most rural Arab males, and for some of their urban cousins as well. The nomads' life and that of their stock has frequently been precarious and always dependent on access to water and scarce grazing. Over-large flocks of subsidised domestic stock are now concentrated on all the best pastures. Apart from direct competition and hunting, wild herbivores became more vulnerable to stress and disease and these pressures are likely to have contributed to their long-term decline.

As stocking rates have risen and a wood-burning human population has increased, there has also been a massive degradation of the vegetation. Although this has accelerated in the last 30 years, such degradation has been in progress, albeit slowly at times, over many centuries. It has happened on such a sweeping scale that it must be very difficult for people to conceive that much of the poverty of their surroundings is man-made. This is reinforced by the perception of man's relationship to nature being framed in a religious context. This is unavoidable because the culture as a whole, and especially education, has a religious base.

Muslims see God as creator of all, the Cherisher and Sustainer of the Worlds, and Islam requires humility, piety and acceptance of God's will. God, not man, holds the ultimate responsibility for Order in the natural world. In this way, Islam claims to have a comprehensive view of the universe, of man and nature, so conservation in Islamic countries must come to terms with the Koran's teachings. In any event, the scriptures will for a long time yet be the major influence on a Muslim's attitude to wildlife.

Because of this religious influence, there is a predisposition to belittle the ecologist's pronouncements on the nature of Nature. It also sees the conservationists' criticisms of practices and attitudes that have sustained the Arabs for thousands of years as naïve presumptuousness. Similar scepticism exists among Christians and Westerners, especially in business circles with development interests. Conservationists should appreciate that what in Western eyes looks like Arab apathy towards Nature and our responsibilities towards Nature is grounded in deeply held religious attitudes.

As global environmental consciousness has spread, theologians have hastened to show that Islam's attitude towards man's relationship to Nature and natural resources is a wise and positive one. The Department of Islamic Studies at Jeddah University has published a paper on Islamic principles for conservation. The authors quote an injunction from the Koran to do no mischief on an earth that has been set in order by God. The universe has been created in due proportion, by measure and in a state of balance.

The earth is man's inheritance, which must be maintained for future generations while serving the interests of the present 'within limits dictated by honesty'. Honesty and justice for all, for man and for Nature, are supposed to be guiding principles in the Muslim dealings with Nature. The fatalism manifest in trusting to God's omnipotent mercy is therefore balanced by the injunction to act within an ethical framework.

Of course there are strong secular influences in Arabia but, unlike Islam, there are fewer mechanisms for the resolution of contradictions. Arabia's prosperity started with the exploitation of a single resource by foreign commercial interests that were devoid of any ethical constraints towards the Arabian environment. That inheritance is only just beginning to change. When the Arab states took command of their own resources, this found immediate expression in buildings and institutions that stood for their own traditional interests and culture, religion and sport. The disbursement of new wealth included massive subsidies for beduin nomads. The perception that the desert, its fauna and flora are victims of 'progress' and that a deeper inheritance is being lost has been slower to develop, but is happening. It is possible that many in the populace share this perception, but the authority to act upon it has to come from above. Both Saudi Arabia and Oman are absolute monarchies and all major initiatives are of royal origin. Only kings and princes, or great sheikhs, actually make things happen.

HM Sultan Qaboos bin Said of Oman has been an outstanding leader in this respect. More recently, HH Prince Saud al Faizal has become the leading figure in conservation in Saudi Arabia. In Bahrain, HH Crown Prince Hammad has built an ambitious nature reserve and park with a research and education programme at Al Areen. Oil money has therefore begun to be invested in the rehabilitation of indigenous habitats and their wildlife.

This year, HH Prince Saud al Faizal hosted an international conference on wildlife conservation in Saudi Arabia under the auspices of the newly formed National Commission for Wildlife Conservation and Development (NCWCD). Visitors and locals were roughly at par and a major target of this conference was the setting up of a National Conservation Action Plan. A preoccupation with animals of the chase—Oryx, Gazelle, Houbara Bustard *Chlamydotis undulata* and birds of prey—might have had some correspondence with the nearly all-male composition of the conference! This is not altogether surprising when the 'macho' up-bringing of males is taken into account. Men tend to be educated towards activity, and the plant world has been neglected by most education systems everywhere. The need for conservation education, however, was widely acknowledged and, if implemented, should reach that 50% of the population who have no contact with hunting and very little with other outdoor pursuits—women.

The urgent need for botanical surveys, botanical research and botanical conservation in Arabia could get a great boost if girls were given special incentives in this direction. Education and entertainment should combine in a country where citizens currently tend to have a lot of spare time. Films, competitions, demonstrations of traditional sports, nature parks, field education centres are all developing rapidly, on the drawing board, or being discussed; zoos have a huge public turnover wherever they exist. The Doha Zoo in Qatar draws in over half the total population, and there are other immensely popular zoos in the Gulf states and Riyadh.

Among its rapidly proliferating duties and opportunities, the NCWCD in Saudi Arabia is charged with the re-introduction of Arabian Oryx and gazelle. In spite of Oman's success on the Jiddat al Harasis, there are formidable difficulties in Saudi Arabia. A major obstacle is the conflict of interests between the nomads' flocks and wildlife. The solution to this problem that has been pursued on the Jiddat al Harasis in Oman has been very simple: to make custodianship of wild animals more prestigious and more financially rewarding than the care of domestic stock. Relatively barren localities that are the traditional pastures of small tribes and capable of supporting only small numbers of stock clearly offer the best opportunity for this sort of switch in values. Plans are in hand for re-introduction of Arabian Oryx and gazelle (along similar lines to those in Harasis) to take place in Saudi Arabia. Where tribes are relatively impoverished, there is a chance that they too might welcome the re-introduction if sufficient incentives are offered. Unlike the isolated Harasis, however, most Saudi sites are surrounded on all sides by competing pastoral nomads and fencing will almost certainly be necessary.

It may be thought that royal authority is enough to persuade the beduin. That this must be qualified was demonstrated when HM King Khalid of Saudi Arabia first fenced in a part of his farm at Thumamah (north of Riyadh) to keep gazelles, Oryx, Ostrich and other wild animals. Beduin shepherds saw the fences as obstructing their traditional grazing rights and broke them down. In the discussions that followed, the beduins were eventually persuaded that rehabilitation of antelopes was in the interest of all Saudis and compensation was accepted. The direct involvement of royalty in this persuasion illustrates how royal patronage has to be the key to most conservation programmes in Saudi Arabia, Oman and other states with traditional rulers. This is not a uniquely Arabian situation; Prince Philip and Prince Bernhard have probably contributed as much to practical conservation in Western Europe as the leading ecologists and naturalists—how much more so in absolute monarchies.

South Yemen is, of course, another situation altogether. It has not been visited recently by Western scientists, has suffered a lethal civil war, and might have the richest fauna and flora in the peninsula, if only it could be studied.

The role of the foreign conservationist in Arabia is essentially that of a short-term guest, contributing experience from elsewhere towards a uniquely Arabian and Muslim enterprise. His or her contribution takes place within Arab political structures, which are mostly incorporated in aristocratic kingdoms. It should also be remembered that conservation is not a new concept in Arabia. The traditional 'hema' system controlled grazing on a seasonal basis and effectively kept some land in reserve status, sometimes as hunting preserves. Ancient awareness of ecological cause and effect is also illustrated by the mythology of Mesopotamia. About 5,000 years ago, Gilgamesh, King of Sumer, is thought to have mounted an expedition to collect timber and stone for the city of Uruk (between Basrah and Baghdad), there being no such resources in the Euphrates Valley. The Cedar forests at the headwaters of the Euphrates were believed to be under the protection of Enlil, a deity who symbolised the forces of Nature and mastery over the fates of men. Enlil's main weapon was floods. In the legends, Gilgamesh triumphs over the guardian of the forests, only to end his days in misery after various lessons from the Gods in his own mortality.

The 'hema' system and traditional awareness of the fragility of desert ecosystems has broken down under the impact of Western technology. Oil, as well as bringing great wealth, is the most recent and the most thorough cause, both direct and indirect, of environmental impoverishment in Arabia. It is very much to the credit of some present leaders, and an indictment on the shortsightedness of most of the large oil companies, that conservation is, only now in the 1980s, beginning to get going in Arabia.

18. Differences in the Response of Populations of Arabian Tahr and Arabian Gazelle to Protection from Hunting in Northern Oman

Paul Munton

Introduction and objectives

In 1978 the author completed a two-year study of the Arabian Tahr in Oman, when a number of areas containing significant populations of the species were described (Munton, 1978; 1979; 1986). The objectives of this three-week field study were to assess the changes in populations of Arabian Tahr *Hemitragus jayakari* and Arabian

Figure 18.1: Map of Wadi Sarin Nature Reserve

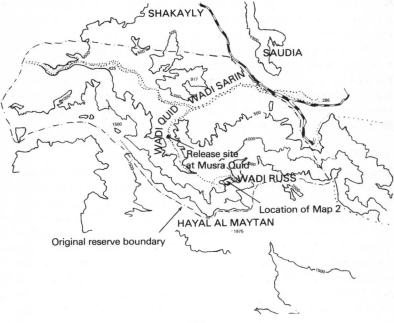

Gazelle *Gazella gazella cora* in certain areas of the north of Oman since 1978.

A breeding centre for the Arabian Gazelle had been set up at Muzra Quid in 1976 in the Wadi Sarin Nature Reserve (Figure 18.1). The original animals came from a number of sources in northern Oman; some were brought in by bedu, others had been presented after it became illegal to possess Gazelle, and some had been pets. After initial problems with nematode parasites had been overcome and mature males had been separated to prevent fighting, the population had bred freely and releases had started in 1979. No detailed records of releases had been kept, but the Tahr guards and the Advisor on Conservation of the Environment in the Diwan of the Royal Court report that between 50 and 60 Gazelles had been released into the surrounding area by February 1987.

Methods

Part of the area of Tahr and Gazelle habitat formerly studied and mapped between 1976 and 1978 was inspected on foot and evidence of the presence of Gazelle and Tahr recorded. Both species make distinctive scrapes in the ground. Those made by Tahr may be 2 metres in length, up to 0.5 metres deep and contain hoof marks, hair and sometimes faeces. Gazelle scrapes are smaller and usually have piles of faeces nearby.

The Tahr guards have recorded seeing Tahr during patrols into the precipitous part of the mountains. Records of sightings of Gazelle have also been made by the guards as and when they came across these animals in the course of their work. These records were translated from the Arabic by the author and used to elucidate population trends for Tahr and Gazelle.

Study Areas

The prime study area was part of the Wadi Sarin Nature Reserve, which consists of a steep rocky limestone cliff running from 300 metres in height to a maximum of 2,000 metres, together with its associated foothills and wadi systems, notably the Wadi Sarin itself and its tributary, the Wadi Quid. Most of the work took place in the Wadi Quid and one of its tributaries, the Wadi Russ. There are no records for rainfall in the area, but records from other nearby mountains in Oman suggest that it would probably be between 150 and 300 millilitres each year. This is rather higher than the coastal rainfall, which varies from about 40 millilitres on Masirah Island to

100 millilitres in Muscat. At low altitudes, the vegetation is dominated by *Acacia tortilis* and *Maerua crassifolia*, but above 1,000 metres there is a mix of African, Asian and Mediterranean plants such as *Olea africana*, *Reptonia buxifolia* and *Ceratonia oreothauma*.

A second area was also visited. This was the coastal strip between the villages of Bimmah and Fins. This is a flat coastal plain bisected by steep-walled wadis dominated by *Acacia tortilis* and *Ziziphus spina-christi*.

Results

During the period 1976 to 1978, Gazelles were seen only once at low level in the foothills and this was southeast of the Wadi Quid. There was also at that time a resident pair close to Hayal al Meytan on the plateau top at 1,750 metres altitude. Observations in 1987 showed that Gazelle scrapes were widespread and were to be found on most flat areas in the foothills of the Jabal Aswad. Those scrapes were not observed in 1978 and are probably due to the successful establishment of Gazelles liberated from the pens at Muzra Quid.

Figure 18.2: Location of scrapes made by Arabian Tahr

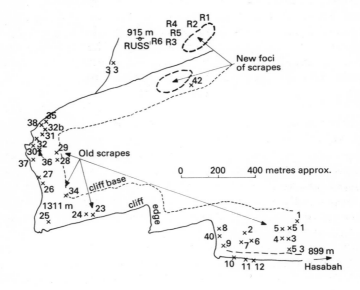

One area of the Wadi Sarin Reserve had been mapped and its use assessed in the 1976–78 study. This area was re-examined, although all the scrape numbers made had since disappeared. All groups of scrapes (foci) seen in 1976 to 1978 were still clearly in use by Tahr. These are shown in Figure 18.2, where individual scrapes are numbered from the 1976–78 study and in which new groups of scrapes are indicated by the dotted circle.

It was also clear that individual scrapes 26, 27 and 32 were still in use, and have probably been so for at least 11 years. In addition, a group of new scrapes had appeared in the vicinity of scrape 42, but it was not clear if this was an extension of the foci of scrapes 23 to 35 or if it was a new foci set up by new animals. There were also three large scrapes present in Wadi Russ and another close to the waterhole. This foci included the faeces of a young Tahr of about six months of age, suggesting that it was a separate foci used by a male, female and young. The numbered scrapes R1 to R6 in Figure 18.2 had been used for no more than a month in 1977.

Although similar habitat is occupied by Tahr in other areas of Oman, no Tahr scrapes were seen at lower levels in the foothills, suggesting that the Tahr either have not filled up the excess areas within the steep mountain areas or that the competition with domestic livestock and Gazelle in these lower areas is too great to allow them to do so.

Four Tahrs were seen on the very steep cliffs just below the mapped area. These were dispersed, with a lone white male, a lone female which was rather inactive and may have been sick, and a pair of animals, one of which was a female and the other either a second female or a young male.

Tahr Guards' Records

The Tahr guards have kept records of Tahr sightings since at least August 1982. The information comprises the number of Tahr and/or Gazelle seen on any one day, the date and place. There is no information on how systematically the data were collected or how complete they are, but there is no reason to doubt the accuracy of records for any specified day and this allows some elementary analysis to be carried out.

Number of Young

The number of young animals seen is a good indicator of the reproductive activity within a population. Bedu regard young animals as those below a year of age. In this case, the number of young seen was counted and expressed as a percentage of the total number of females seen. From 12 August 1982 to 7 March 1987, 106 young and 223 females were seen; thus, 47.5% of the females were associated with young animals. As the tendency of small young animals to spend more time resting or lying in caves makes them more difficult to see than the females, this is likely to be an underestimate of total young and suggests that the population is reproducing quite well.

Changes in Number of Tahrs

The mean number of animals seen per observation day for each year from 1982 to 1987 was calculated by adding up the number of animals seen in a year and dividing that by the number of days on which there were recorded sightings of Tahr. This exercise was carried out on the basis of total Tahr seen, young Tahr and adult Tahr. The data and results are as follows:

Table 18.1: Sightings of Tahr

	1982 (4 months)	1983	1984	1985	1986	1987 (3 months)
No. of days on which Tahr seen	8	63	42	57	37	19
Total Tahr seen	16	133	119	141	93	59
Mean seen per day	2	2.11	2.83	2.47	2.5	3.1
Mean young per day	0.375	0.476	0.619	0.315	0.405	0.632
Mean adults per day	1.63	1.64	2.21	2.12	2.11	2.48

The general trend is upwards but with high levels of sightings of all classes of Tahr in 1984. If all three sets of scores are plotted and the best curve taken, the overall rate of increase is 6% per year with a barely perceptible increase over the period for young animals.

An attempt was made to assess the reproductive rate of Tahr females in the population. To do this, a model was constructed to simulate population growth of 6%. It was assumed that the population remained at a constant level from 1961 until conservation measures were taken in 1977; that the sex ratio within the population is not significantly biased (Munton, 1986); that females bred in their third year, as in many wild goat populations; that life expectancy was 15 years (equivalent to the age of the oldest Tahr horns found in the 1976–78 study); and that the founder population consisted of equal age classes. The population in any year was based on the formula $(((n-2.r)/2)+n-1)-(0.067.n-15)$ where n-2, n-1, n-15 are populations two, one and 15 years previously and r is the reproductive success of a female in the population expressed as the number of breeding animals she contributed to the population in her lifetime. It was found that the rise in total population most closely approximated to 6% when r = 0.23. It is unlikely that the age classes in the founder population were equal, and other calculations assuming fewer animals in the older classes were found to reduce the value of r.

At first sight, a reproductive success rate of 0.23 is at variance with the observation of high numbers of young in the mountains, but if correct it could indicate a low survival rate between weaning, at probably eight months of age, and maturity at two or three years of age. An alternative hypothesis is that young Tahr are migrating out of the reserve, but, as there are clearly considerable areas of under-used resources, it would be expected that these would be utilised before the animals migrated.

Munton (1986) calculated the the Tahr population in the Wadi Sarin Reserve had been suffering an annual loss from hunting of between 17.5% and 20%. Assuming that a reproductive rate for females of 0.23 would have just about kept pace with mortality caused by hunting, the rise in population of 6% a year may be due to relief from hunting pressures.

At these rates of reproduction the total Tahr population of the reserve would double only every 10 to 12 years, rising slowly from the 360 calculated in 1978 to 600 at present, and to 750 in 1990 and 1,600 at the turn of the century, assuming that other factors did not affect the situation. Such a rate of increase between 1978 and 1987 is consistent with the rise in Tahr scrape activity observed in the study area and the observation that Tahr have not spread onto lower grounds or onto the plateau.

Gazelle Observations

The observations by the Tahr guards show that Gazelle occupy an extensive area of the Wadi Sarin Reserve, including the low hills to the north of the Wadi Sarin itself (Al Khoban). Gazelle have also

Table 18.2: Numbers of Gazelle seen recorded by guards in and around Wadi Sarin (excludes coastal populations)

	1982	1983	1984	1985	1986	1987
No. of days on which Gazelle seen	7	31	64	73	64	19
Total Gazelle seen corrected to 1 year	29 (87)	115	208	208	236	63 (252)
Figures from common origin (Fig. 18.3)	2	2.64	4.87	4.8	5.43	5.79
Mean seen per day	4.1	3.7	3.3	2.9	3.7	3.3

been seen in the steep mountains at Qablat Sufr, part of the main Tahr study area, but it is not clear if these are resident individuals or animals moving through the area. Gazelle have also been recorded east of the tarmac road (Saudia) and regularly near the house of one of the Tahr guards over 10 kilometres from the release site. Gazelle were not being reported from these areas in 1978 and their ubiquity may be associated with the release programme at Musra Quid, or with the effects of conservation activities of the Tahr guards on pre-existing wild Gazelle.

The figures in Table 18.2 differ in form from those obtained for Tahr because, although there is a steady increase in the numbers of Gazelle seen each year, there is no trend in the number of Gazelle seen each day. The probable reason for this is that most Tahr sightings are the result of visits to different parts of the mountain massif with the intention of seeing Tahr. The Gazelle data, on the other hand, are the result of casual encounters during day-to-day activity of the Tahr guards, or of encounters when searching for Tahr. Sightings of Gazelle are less likely during searches for Tahr because of the observed habitat separation between the two species. The lack of change in number of animals seen per day also suggests that Gazelle in the mountains form small groups which, above a threshold, are somewhat independent of the population size of the reserve. If the daily records of Gazelle are plotted, the curve shows that there was a steep increase in total numbers of Gazelle observed from 1982 to 1984, which subsequently continued

Figure 18.3: Relative increases in numbers of Arabian Gazelle and Arabian Tahr

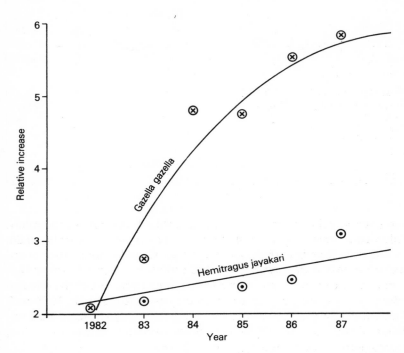

at a much lower rate. This would be consistent with a rapid build-up of the Gazelle as released animals bred to fill up existing habitat.

The relative increases in Gazelle and Tahr numbers have been compared by scaling down the figures for Gazelle to give the same origin (i.e. total Gazelle seen per year/43.5). The curves for Gazelle and Tahr are plotted in Figure 18.3.

Gazelle on Coast between Bimmah and Tiwi

A small population existed in this coastal strip in 1978, but fewer than five Gazelle were seen during an inspection of the area in 1978. During a two-day visit on 5 and 6 March 1987, only a small part of the area was inspected but in 30 minutes a number of small groups were seen totalling 22 animals. A further 39 animals were seen the following day in small groups. Clearly this population has risen considerably in numbers, and probably as a result of the active anti-hunting work by Tahr guards.

Conclusions

It is obvious even from the relatively sparse amount of data gleaned from this brief study that Gazelle numbers in the Wadi Sarin area increased rapidly up to 1985 and at a slower rate to date (Figure 18.3). An expansion of the population has also occurred in the coastal strip between Tiwi and Bimmah. There is insufficient information at present to estimate just how large that increase has been. It is clear, however, that in the Wadi Sarin the restocking programme has been successful in putting a population of Gazelle into an area where there was not a significant foundation population.

These Gazelle have occupied the foothills of the Jabal Aswad and spread beyond the reserve boundary. Protection by the Tahr guards has undoubtedly helped the survival of the population. More work is needed to estimate numbers of Gazelle established in the reserve and the extent of their spread both within and beyond the reserve boundaries. The Gazelle seem to be co-existing with present levels of domestic livestock using the foothills, suggesting that in the past hunting has been the major factor preventing survival of high numbers of the species in the area. Exposure to people in the pens at Quid prior to liberation seems to have resulted in the animals being prepared to use areas close to sites of human activity, such as the guard house of the Tahr guards in the reserve, and this may be one reason why Gazelle now use the same areas as goats in the reserve.

In the coastal area behind Fins, work by the Tahr guards has undoubtedly resulted in protection of the foundation population seen in 1978 and allowed its expansion to present levels. As there are very few goats in the area and local densities of *Acacia tortilis* are high, it seems likely that the area could support a population in the order of 500 to 1,000 Gazelle. The limiting factor will be the seasonality of the productivity of *Acacia* and the extent to which the whole tree is available to the Gazelle, which is a rather small ungulate.

The paucity of Gazelle in other mountain areas visited suggests that protection from hunting and disturbance may be the key to their survival. Being adapted to an arid environment, the species is not dependent on free water and may therefore be able to compete successfully with goats or at least hold its own in its preferred habitat.

The picture for the Arabian Tahr is rather different. It is possible to say that there is no evidence for decline in Tahr numbers in Wadi Sarin, Jebel Nakhal or Jabal Sartri. There is evidence from surveys of Tahr scrapes that there has been a rise in the population in the Wadi Sarin and that new foci of scrapes are being set up by pairs of Tahr. Over the last ten years, the rise in numbers under a protective regime similar to that for Gazelle has not been large enough for pressure of numbers to cause the Tahrs to expand into the foothills below; indeed, there seems to be a lot of spare capacity in the steep mountains of the Wadi Sarin. The records of the Tahr guards seem to show a slight but consistent rise over the period 1982–87 in the number of Tahr recorded as sighted on any one day (Figure 18.3). This rise would be consistent with a small annual rise in population of the order of 6% over the period and a longer-term trend of the population doubling every 10 to 12 years. Although caution is necessary in the interpretation of the Tahr guards' data, this assessment seems reasonable in the light of all data obtained during the study.

Little is known about the ecology of the Arabian Gazelle or about the extent to which it competes with the domestic goat. It is not clear if the Gazelle in Wadi Sarin survive in competition because there is enough for both goats and Gazelle or because they are feeding on different plants. Work on the Tahr (Munton, 1986) has shown that it has a similar diet to the domestic goat. The species is not found in apparently suitable areas frequently used by goats, but this may be because it is sensitive to disturbance rather than because it cannot compete for food. Nevertheless, in the Wadi Sarin Reserve, there are areas of suitable Tahr habitat that appear to be unoccupied, so there may be no pressure on the animal to enter foothill areas where they would be in competition with domestic goats and more subject to disturbance. Gazelle would be under such pressure because their preferred habitat is the foothills and plateaux rather then the precipitous mountains where Tahr are found. It is on the easier terrain of such plateaux and foothills that the bedu prefer to live and browse their goats.

In general, the different rates of recovery shown by the Gazelle and Tahr populations may be said to be due to their different reproduction rates and to differences in their capacity to exploit their environments once the pressure of hunting has been removed. The truly arid-adapted species, the Gazelle, has expanded rapidly after being protected. On the other hand, the Tahr has shown a slow expansion, perhaps related to its status as a relict with many of the characteristics of a temperate species, a dependency on free water and the availability of a wide variety of succulent leaves, fruits or seeds, and with a need for caves in which to shelter (Munton, 1986).

References

Munton, P.N. (1978) Final Report on ICUN/WWF joint project 1290, *The Conservation of the Arabian Tahr*. IUCN, Gland, Switzerland (Mimeograph).

Munton, P.N. (1979) Arabian Tahr in Oman. *Oryx XV* (2): 145–7.

Munton, P.N. (1986) The ecology of the Arabian Tahr (*Hemitragus jayakari*, Thomas, 1894) and a strategy for the conservation of the species. *J. Oman Studies 8* (1): 11–48.

19. A Catalogue of the Genus *Gazella*

Colin P. Groves

Introduction

The bovid fauna of the Arabian Peninsula is impoverished and numbers only some 12 species, of which half are gazelles. It is therefore not surprising that, collectively, gazelles used to be the most abundant and widely distributed of Arabia's bovids and that they were also the best adapted to use all the major habitats of the peninsula (even their common names 'Sand Gazelle' and 'Mountain Gazelle' are suggestive of this partitioning). Specific radiation into particular niches is even more advanced in Africa and Central Asia and has given rise to a wider variety of morphological types than is found in Arabia. As a result, the taxonomy of the genus is somewhat complicated and, in some cases, uncertain.

In recent years, local interest in gazelles has switched from hunting to keeping. This is a welcome change of attitude, but brings with it the threat of genetic contamination or hybridisation for populations that may be extinct in the wild (notably the Saudi Gazelle). It is therefore important that gazelles, whether wild, feral or in captivity, should be correctly identified and, wherever possible, be prohibited from interbreeding artificially with other species or races.

The genus *Gazella* is almost certainly polyphyletic; other members of the bovid tribe Antilopini may be closer to one or other species group of *Gazella*. Until further study can indicate how the genus should be split up, the multiplicity of species can be divided among five informal species groups:

Group 1: The central group of *Gazella*: includes *G. dorcas* (the type species), *G. saudiya*, *G. gazella*, *G. bilkis*, *G. arabica*, *G. spekei* and *G. bennetti*.

Group 2: Gazelles of the sand dunes: G. *subgutturosa* and G. *leptoceros*.

Group 3: The enigmatic species G. *cuvieri*.

Group 4: Gazelles of more mesic, less arid environments: G. *rufifrons* (which includes the well-known Thomson's Gazelle as a subspecies) and G. *rufina*.

Group 5: The giant gazelles: G. *dama*, G. *soemmerringi* and G. *granti*.

All species are here described except for G. *rufina*, which is probably extinct (former range: some part of northern Algeria), and G. *arabica*, known only from Farasan Island in the Red Sea, which is poorly known and currently under investigation.

Gazella bennetti

Bennett's or Indian Gazelle; Chinkara.

Identification: tawny colour, very poorly marked face and body stripes; straight horns, well ringed in male, long and well formed in female.

Distribution: southern Iran, Pakistan and northern India.

Geographic variation: several subspecies; larger, darker in hilly regions, smaller and pale in arid areas.

Conservation status: protected in Gujarat, Rajasthan; elsewhere, status is uncertain.

Gazella bilkis

Queen of Sheba's Gazelle.

Identification: very dark; rather large; short ears; male's horns short, thick and nearly straight; female's horns long.

Distribution: mountains of North Yemen.

Conservation status: uncertain, but apparently still occurs in the wild.

Notes: This species was described only in 1975. In some respects, it closely resembles *Gazella gazella gazella*, and may be conspecific if the relationship of *G.g.cora* (with which it is sympatric) could be clarified. There are specimens at Chester Zoo.

Gazella cuvieri

Cuvier's or Atlas Mountain Gazelle.

Identification: dark grey-brown; flank band dark brown; horns long and well ringed in both sexes.

194

Distribution: Atlas and neighbouring ranges in Morocco, Algeria and Tunisia, to the lowlands in western Morocco.
Conservation status: rare, perhaps endangered.

Gazella dama

Dama or Addra Gazelle.
Identification: legs, flanks and nose predominantly white; horns simple, S-shaped.
Distribution: Sahara (west of River Nile).
Geographic variation: reduction in the amount of red from west to east; this cline is 'stepped' at intervals (especially in eastern Chad), so that three or four subspecies can be recognised.
Conservation status: very much endangered in most of its range.

Gazella dorcas

Dorcas Gazelle (including Pelzeln's Gazelle).
Identification: small; well-marked face stripes, but flank stripe poorly marked; long ears; horns S-shaped, incurved at tips in both sexes.
Distribution: circum-Saharan zone of North Africa to Mediterranean seaboard, Sudan, coast of northern Somalia and Ethiopia, Sinai, southern Israel.
Geographic variation: sandy-coloured forms west of the Nile, redder-toned east of the Nile. About six subspecies, some well distinguished.
Conservation status: becoming rare in many parts of its range, but generally the commonest gazelle wherever it occurs. Protected and not uncommon in Israeli, Somalian and Tunisian parts of its range.

Gazella gazella

Arabian/Palestine Mountain Gazelle; Common Arabian Gazelle.
Identification: fairly well marked with flank and face stripes and strong contrast between light haunch and dark croup; long legs; long tail; horns short and stout in male, small and fragile in female.
Distribution: Arabian Peninsula, Israel, Lebanon, ?Syria.
Geographic variation: sharply distinct subspecies in (1) Israel/Lebanon mountains (*G.g.gazella*) and (2) Arabian Peninsula (*G.g.cora*). The latter may be more correctly referred to *G. dorcas*. Also (3) *G.g.muscatensis* (Oman).

Conservation status: *G.g.gazella* common, protected; *G.g.cora* rare, but survives in suitable habitats, especially the mountains along the east side of the Red Sea; *G.g.muscatensis* apparently still locally common in Oman mountains.

Gazella granti

Grant's Gazelle.

Identification: sandy-fawn; white wedge into haunch; long white face stripes; very long, divergent horns in both sexes (shorter in female).

Distribution: northern Tanzania, Kenya, into borders of Uganda, Sudan, Ethiopia, Somalia.

Geographic variation: several well-marked subspecies differing in size, horn shape, presence of flank band and colour of tail.

Conservation status: common, protected in Kenya and Tanzania; elsewhere uncertain.

Gazella leptoceros

Slender-horned Gazelle or African Sand Gazelle.

Identification: very pale, poorly marked; horns very long, little curved, in both sexes.

Distribution: sand-dune regions of Sahara (west of River Nile).

Conservation status: uncertain, but reported to be nearly extinct in Egypt; may be protected to some extent by the nature of its habitat.

Gazella rufifrons

Red-fronted Gazelle (including Thomson's, Mongalla and Heuglin's Gazelles).

Identification: reddish colour, with black flank band and well-marked face stripes; horns of male prominently ringed, of female short and fragile.

Distribution: southern borders of Sahara, from Senegal to northern Ethiopia; Sudan, east of Nile; Kenya; northern Tanzania.

Geographic variations: several well-marked subspecies: (1) *G.r.rufifrons* (Senegal), bright red; (2) *G.r.laevipes* (Niger to River Nile), less bright tone; (3) *G.r.kanuri* (southern Chad), small, cinnamon -coloured; (4) *G.r. tilonura* (northwestern Ethiopia; Heuglin's or Black-tailed Gazelle), hooked horns; (5) *G.r.albonotata* (southern Sudan, east of Nile; Mongalla Gazelle), thicker black flank stripe, white on forehead; (6) *G.r.thomsoni* (Kenya, Tanzania), thick flank stripe with no red band below it, cinnamon colour, very long horns in male; (7) *G.r.nasalis* (Kenya, west of Rift Valley, and northwestern Tanzania), smaller, darker-faced. These last two (6 and 7) are together known as Thomson's Gazelle.

Conservation status: common only in Kenya and Tanzania; elsewhere endangered.

Gazella saudiya

Saudi Gazelle.

Identification: smallest gazelle; sandy-brown, almost no body markings; short legs; very big ears; short tail; horns very long, nearly straight, those of female as long as those of male.

Distribution: flat desert areas of Saudi Arabia, Kuwait, southern Iraq.

Conservation status: seems to be extinct in the wild. Re-introduction in Saudi Arabia recently proposed, but only captive examples so far identified are 15 in Bahrain, 50+ in Al Ain Zoo, United Arab Emirates.

Notes: This has commonly been referred to as *Gazella dorcas saudiya*, but it seems sharply distinct and there is no sign of intergradation. The Common Arabian Gazelle, currently called *Gazella gazella cora*, seems more likely to be the Arabian representative of *G. dorcas*.

Gazella soemmerringi

Soemmerring's Gazelle.

Identification: white wedge into haunch; blackish midface; hooked horns.

Distribution: Sudan (east of River Nile), Somalia, Ethiopia.

Geographic variation: larger, darker in Somalia; paler, smaller elsewhere.

Conservation status: endangered in most parts of its range.

Gazella spekei

Speke's Gazelle.

Identification: strongly marked black flank stripe, face stripes; S-shaped horns; inflatable skin on nose.

Distribution: desert zone of Somalia and eastern Ethiopia.

Conservation status: locally fairly common.

Gazella subgutturosa

Goitred Gazelle (including Persian, Mongolian and Arabian Sand Gazelles).

Identification: rather heavily built; male with (cartilaginous) lump in throat; male's horns long, lyrate, female's may be absent; indistinct flank and face stripes; nose, and sometimes whole face, largely white.

Distribution: Saudi Arabia, Jordan, southeast Turkey east to Pakistan, northeast via Soviet Central Asia to Mongolia, Ordos and Caidam.

Geographic variation: several well-marked subspecies, including (1) *G.s.subgutturosa* (Iran, Pakistan, Turkmenia), fawn, female usually hornless; (2) *G.s.hillieriana* (Mongolian and Chinese parts of range), pale sandy, females hornless, male's horns shorter; (3) *G.s.marica* (western Asian parts of range), known as Sand Gazelle or Rheem (Rhim), very pale and small, female has horns.

Conservation status: still common in Mongolia, USSR; in Arabia it has survived better than other gazelles, probably because of its preference for sandy areas; elsewhere its status is uncertain.

The recognition that *G. saudiya*, *G. bilkis* and *G. arabica* may be full species within the central *Gazella* group not only enlarges the Arabian fauna, but brings with it the need for more precise definitions of the morphology, adaptive physiology, diet, ecology and original geographic range of all gazelles and Arabian species in particular. If samples of Arabia's many and varied habitats are to be rehabilitated (or even re-created), further study of these species in the wild and in captivity will be necessary. It is also important that rare or extinct species that are in captivity should be studied and propagated, with fuller recognition of their biological and conservation value.

20. Captive Populations of Northwest African Antilopinae and Caprinae at the Estacion Experimental de Zonas Aridas

C.L. Alados, Juan Escos and Juan-Ramon Vericad

Since 1971, one of the major research programmes of the Arid Zone Experimental Station (Estacion Experimental de Zonas Aridas), a Research Institute of the Scientific Research Council of Spain (Consejo Superior de Investigaciones Cientificas), has been the captive breeding of endangered North African Antilopinae and Caprinae. The sharp decline of local populations of Dama Gazelle *Gazella dama*, Dorcas Gazelle *G. dorcas* and Cuvier's Gazelle *G. cuvieri*, as well as of Aoudad *Ammotragus lervia*, was recognised by Professor Valverde as a threat to the continued existence of these particular subspecies. As a result, specimens were collected from known localities of Western Sahara. Almeria was considered the most suitable location for the captive-breeding programme because of its climate, which is very similar to that of North Africa.

The objectives of the captive-breeding programme are as follows:

(a) To establish and maintain studbooks for *Gazella dama*, *G. cuvieri*, *G. dorcas* and *Ammotragus lervia* and to conduct biological, veterinary and behavioural studies on these species.

(b) To supply breeding herds for conservation purposes to zoos and to field units in northwest African countries as a means of restocking populations and maintaining genetic diversity. Minimum conditions required in the new locations are suitable facilities for the animals, permanent staff and adequate budgets.

(c) To contribute to re-introduction projects by offering animals of the species concerned, scientific support and specialised staff.

Status and Distribution of the Species

The original distribution of *Ammotragus lervia* was the mountains and low hills of the desert zone throughout most of the Sahara,

Captive Populations of Antilopinae and Caprinae

from the Western Sahara to the Red Sea coast and south from the Mediterranean coastal areas. In the south, the limit coincided with the southern boundary of the sub-desert steppe of the Sudanese arid zone (Keay, 1959).

Six subspecies of Aoudad are described by Ansell (1971): *A.l. lervia* (Pallas, 1777), living in northern Algeria and northern Tunisia (including *tragelaphus*, Cuvier, 1817); *A.l. fasini* Lepri, 1930, found in Libya; *A.l. ornata* (Audouin, 1829), in Egypt; *A.l. blainei* (Roths-child, 1913), in northern Sudan and in Chad in the Ennedi and Uweinat mountains; *A.l. angusi* (Rothschild, 1921), in the Air and Asben, in Niger west to the Adrar des Iforhas of Algeria and east to Tibesti in Chad; and *A.l. sahariensis* (Rothschild, 1913), in southern Algeria. Exact limits to both the southwest and southeast are unknown. The form occurring in Western Sahara and Mauritania is not confirmed according to Harper (1945), although he identified it provisionally as *sahariensis*. The population of Western Sahara is considered extinct by Valverde (1968), Gillet (1969) and Newby (1981a). While the Aoudad in Mauritania is very rare (Newby, 1981a), Mohamed Ould Cheikk recorded animals in the Adrar in 1986.

Gazella dama (Pallas, 1766) is widely distributed in northern Africa in the Sahelian and southern Sahara zones, from south Morocco to Senegal, eastwards through the Hoggar massif in Algeria, Bilma and into Sudan as far as the White Nile. Eight subspecies of Dama Gazelle have been described following Ansell (1971); *G.d. dama* (Pallas, 1766), living in Senegal across to Lake Chad; *G.d. mhorr* (Bennet, 1833), in southwest Morocco and Western Sahara; *G.d. lozanoi* (Morales Agacino, 1934), in Cape Juby, Western Sahara; *G.d. permista* (Neuman 1906), in Senegal; *G.d. reducta* (K. Heller, 1907), locality unknown; *G.d. damergouensis* (Rothschild, 1921), in Damergou; *G.d. weidholzi* (Zimara, 1935), in Hombori; and *G.d. ruficollis* (H. Smith, 1827), in the Darfur and Kordofan Provinces.

Although estimates of numbers are very difficult to make because Dama Gazelles are highly mobile and range over wide areas, Newby (1981b) considered that they were very rapidly decreasing and that this was becoming an endangered species. Before 1978, there was a viable population in the Ouadi Rime-Ouadi Achim Faunal Reserve in Chad, but military activity has forced the cessation of all conservation work in that country. The Air Mountain-Tenere region in Niger appears to support a good

200

population of Dama Gazelle, estimated at 150–250 by Grettenber-ger and Newby (1985). In Morocco, the Dama Gazelle was reported extinct by Chapuis in 1961, although 20 years previously it was present in sub-Saharan wadis in the Dra region and Panouse (1957) reported the presence of Dama Gazelle in the Hamada of Tindouf near Merkala. Boroviczeny (1981) noted that surveys in 1975 indicated the complete absence of Dama Gazelle in Western Sahara, although they were known to occur in Saguia el Hamra.

The general distribution of Cuvier's Gazelle includes the moun-tain regions of Morocco, Algeria and Tunisia. In Morocco, the highest concentrations are in the Anti Atlas Mountains (Aulagnier and Thevenot, in prep.), but their numbers are decreasing in the Saharan Atlas and in the coastal ranges in the west (*Red Data Book*, in press). In Tunisia, the species is protected in the Djebel Chambi Reserve (Willan, 1973).

The Dorcas Gazelle is widely distributed throughout the north-ern parts of Africa to the Somali coast and across the Arabian Peninsula to India and Pakistan. It inhabits the semi-desert plains and even the desert zones of this vast area. The taxonomy of the subspecies of *G. dorcas* has been reviewed by several authors. In Africa, Groves (1981) listed six subspecies and Alados (1987) listed five: *G.d. dorcas* (Linnaeus, 1758), from the southeastern Sahara to central and northeastern Egypt; *G.d. neglecta* (Lavauden, 1926), in Western Sahara; *G.d. massaesyla* (Cabrera, 1928), in the high plat-eaux, north of the Saharan Atlas; *G.d. isabella* (Gray, 1946), on the Red Sea coast; and *G.d. pelzelni* (Kohl, 1886), in Somalia. In Morocco, Dorcas Gazelle are nearly extinct on the Atlantic side of the Atlas mountains, although there are three reserves in the area. In eastern Morocco, south of the Atlantic zones and north of the Oued Dra, Dorcas Gazelle are more numerous. South of the Oued Dra there is little information, although Lobbers (pers. comm.) reported Dorcas Gazelle living in Oued Eddahab.

Husbandry at Almeria

The three species of gazelle at Almeria are distributed in different herds consisting of about 10 to 15 individuals. One of them is an adult male and the remainder are adult females with their off-spring. The young males are kept with their family group until the age of four or five months; thereafter they are grouped into bachelor herds in order to keep them as future reproductive males.

201

By contrast, the Aoudad are all kept together in the same enclosure.

A calf is caught the day after birth in order to be marked and for the collection of biological data. Records are kept of the calf's body measurements, parents' identity and code number. Because of the growth in numbers, however, we are changing to a system of ear-tags using a colour code. This enables us to identify the individual faster for the purposes of research and management.

The enclosure is built of a flexible wire mesh, 2 metres high, with metallic posts and without dangerous right-angled corners where an animal could be caught and injured. There is an indoor house in which the animals can get food and shelter. The enclosures must be large enough for the animals to maintain inter-individual distance and the house must have at least two doors which allow a fast escape for a frightened individual.

As we do not have a big area for the gazelles and the Aoudad, we cannot have enclosures of enormous size. When designing the enclosure, however, we took into account the biological and behavioural characeristics of the species concerned. As a result, the area is provided with shrubs and branches, enabling the offspring to hide and the older individuals to avoid other animals. The branches are also useful as a means of displaying aggression or playfulness. Food is spread out in a big area to avoid conflict.

History of the Populations

Seventeen (4:13) Dama Gazelle, four (2:2) Cuvier's Gazelle, 72 (36:36) Dorcas Gazelle and three (2:1) Aoudad were originally brought to Almeria. Although the numbers for G. dama and G. dorcas represent an acceptable founder population, those for G. cuvieri and A. lervia do not. However, since the maintenance of a species' gene pool is thought to provide the genetic plasticity that increases the chances of successfully surviving in varying environmental conditions (Ryder, 1983, in Benirschke, 1985), care must be taken not to lose these genes. Following Benirschke (1985), the critical factors to be taken into consideration are: introgression, inbreeding, genetic drift, artifical selection and founder effect. With suitable management at Almeria, the potential effect of these factors can be limited.

Table 20.1 presents the number of individuals that died before September 1986 and the number of individuals of both sexes surviving at that date, as well as the sex ratio and reproductive

Table 20.1: Status of the population of Gazelles and Aoudad kept in Almeria (September 1986)

		Males	Females	Sex Ratio	Reproduc-tive index
G.dama	Dead	108	97		
	Alive	25	34		0.50
	Sent to other institutions	17	26		
	Total	150	157	1.05	
G. cuvieri	Dead	70	56		
	Alive	33	31		0.83
	Sent to other institutions	3	8		
	Total	106	95	0.90	
G. dorcas	Dead	185	141		
	Alive	42	72		1.09
	Sent to other institutions	11	19		
	Total	238	232	0.97	
A. lervia	Dead	5	4		
	Alive	9	22		1.25
	Total	14	26	1.86	

index. From this table we can obtain the mortality rate (number of dead divided by total population and multiplied by 100), which is lower for the Aoudad population than for the gazelle populations (22.5% for *A. lervia*, 66.9% for *G. dama*, 62.7% for *G. cuvieri* and 69.4% for *G. dorcas*)) ($X^2=8.91$, df=1, P < 0.01 for Aoudad vs. Dama Gazelle; $X^2=7.54$, df=1, P < 0.01 for Aoudad vs. Cuvier's Gazelle; $X^2=11.66$, df=1, P < 0.001 for Aoudad vs. Dorcas Gazelle). There is no significant difference between the mortality rates of the three species of gazelle ($X^2=0.59$, df=2, N.S.).

Comparisons of the causes of gazelle deaths at Almeria (Figure 20.1) show differences for each of the species ($X^2=106.7$, df=10,

P < 0.001 one-tailed test). With Dorcas Gazelle, the causes were principally traumatic in origin; with Cuvier's, deaths were usually a result of aggression; and in Dama Gazelle pathological-perinatal problems were the most common cause of mortality. Changes in husbandry were also a factor. For example, neither deaths as a result of aggression nor abortions occurred in a herd of 34 female and young Cuvier's Gazelle observed during the first period of their stay at Almeria (39 months). When individuals were exchanged in order to avoid inbreeding, however, the rate of deaths among females as a result of aggression increased dramatically to 44% and the rate of abortions rose to 0.37 (number of abortions/number of females). To avoid this in future, we are studying the competitive behaviour of females.

The sex ratio of the total population for each species does not vary significantly from the expected value 1:1 ($X^2=0.16$, df=1, N.S. for Dama Gazelle; $X^2=0.60$, df=1, N.S. for Cuvier's Gazelle; $X^2=0.08$, df=1, N.S. for Dorcas Gazelle), although in the Aoudad population the difference is nearly significant ($X = 3.6$, df = 1, P < 0.1). The same tendency of the sex ratio imbalance was also observed in a wild population of introduced *A. lervia* living in Sierra Espuna (in the southeast of Spain).

Figure 20.1: Causes of death of *G. dorcas* (D), *G. cuvieri* (C) and *G. dama* (DM) from 1971 to 1986

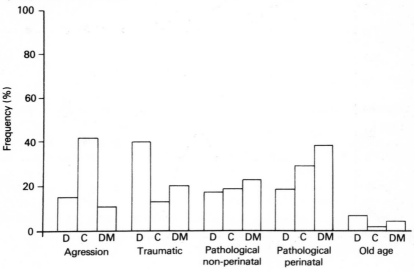

Figure 20.2: Rate of total population change for each species

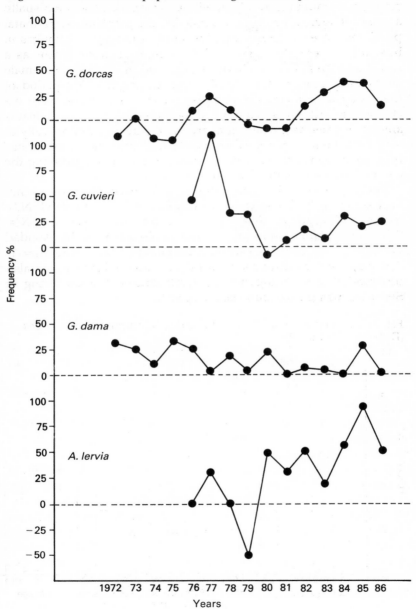

The rate of change of the total population for each of the species studied is presented in Figure 20.2, which shows the percentage of increase or decrease in the population each year based on the difference between the number of births and deaths each year, divided by the total population size and multiplied by 100. Aoudad and Cuvier's Gazelle, both of which have twins, show a high level of oscillation through the years, while Dama and Dorcas Gazelle, with single births, have lower oscillations.

Demography

In general terms, animal collections must be managed as biological populations by applying the principles and methods of demography and genetics, as well as general husbandry and behavioural considerations, to propagation programmes. Demographic methods are possible only if adequate data are available. The minimum essentials (dates of birth and death, sex and parentage) are available from our studbooks, one of which has been endorsed lately (Escos, in press).

Our captive populations are relatively small and their known histories short, so estimates are not always statistically valid. Hence, in the present study, parameters computed for *G. dorcas* or *G. dama* may be more reliable than those for the smaller populations of *G. cuvieri*. Aoudad have not been taken into account because of our small population size. A further factor to be considered is that the parameters for the three species are based on averages calculated over their entire documented history. However, since changes in husbandry or the effects of inbreeding are likely to have affected lifespans and/or fertility, the averages may not always realistically reflect current values. Even under the most stable and optimum conditions, the parameters would be expected to vary a little over time.

Demographic analyses and management require information on three characteristics of a population: age and sex structure; age- and sex-specific survival; age- and sex-specific fertility. To compute the fertility tables, we have used the age-specific survival, l_x. This demographic parameter is estimated from the probability that an animal will survive into some age class (x to x+1) (Chiang, 1984). Tables 20.2, 20.3 and 20.4 show that *G. dama*'s age survival is greater than that of *G. cuvieri* and *G. dorcas*. The low age of survival of *G. cuvieri* has been due to social behaviour problems and management (Escos and Gomendio, 1984; Gomendio and Escos, 1984).

Captive Populations of Antilopinae and Caprinae

Fertility may, and often does, differ significantly for males and females. The sexes can be treated as separate populations (Keyfitz, 1977; Krebs, 1985). Because the husbandry is different for males and females in our centre and principal interest is usually focused on females, we have concentrated on females only.

Table 20.2: Fertility table for *Gazella cuvieri* female population in captivity

Age Group	Midpoint or pivotal age x	Proportion surviving to pivotal age l_x	No. female offspring per female aged x per year (b_x)	Product of l_x and b_x (V_x)	Product $V_x.x$
0.0–1.0	0.5	0.7915	0.0119	0.0094	0.0047
1.0–2.0	1.5	0.8832	0.3600	0.3179	0.47685
2.0–3.0	2.5	0.8450	1.2500	1.0563	2.6407
3.0–4.0	3.5	0.9033	1.9167	1.7313	6.0595
4.0–5.0	4.5	0.8765	0.6000	0.5259	2.3665
5.0–6.0	5.5	0.7633	0.2222	0.1696	0.9328
6+	–	–	–	–	–

$$R_0 = \sum_0^x l_x b_x \qquad \sum_0^x V_x x$$
$$= 3.8106 \qquad = 12.4810$$

Table 20.3: Fertility table for *Gazella dorcas* female population in captivity

Age Group	Midpoint or pivotal age x	Proportion surviving to pivotal age l_x	No. female offspring per female aged x per year (b_x)	Product of l_x and b_x (V_x)	Product $V_x.x$
0.0–1.0	0.5	0.7661	0.0684	0.0524	0.0262
1.0–2.0	1.5	0.8229	0.3846	0.3165	0.4748
2.0–3.0	2.5	0.8598	0.4090	0.3517	0.8793
3.0–4.0	3.5	0.8777	0.2666	0.2340	0.8192
4.0–5.0	4.5	0.8912	0.3636	0.3240	1.4584
5.0–6.0	5.5	0.7933	0.3000	0.2380	1.3090
6.0–7.0	6.6	0.8751	0.6000	0.5251	3.4131
7.0–8.0	7.5	0.6859	0.6000	0.4115	3.0866

$$R_0 = \sum_0^x l_x b_x \qquad \sum_0^x V_x x$$
$$= 2.4535 \qquad = 11.4666$$

Captive Populations of Antilopinae and Caprinae

Table 20.4: Fertility table for *Gazella dama* female population in captivity

Age Group	Midpoint or pivotal age x	Proportion surviving to pivotal age l_x	No. female offspring per female aged x per year (b_x)	Product of l_x and b_x (V_x)	Product $V_x \cdot x$
0.0–1.0	0.5	0.7968	0.0069	0.0050	0.0027
1.0–2.0	1.5	0.8476	0.1136	0.0963	0.1444
2.0–3.0	2.5	0.8133	0.3871	0.3148	0.7871
3.0–4.0	3.5	0.9622	0.4285 ·	0.4124	1.4434
4.0–5.0	4.5	0.9116	0.5384	0.49087	2.2089
5.0–6.0	5.5	0.8911	0.6363	0.5670	3.1189
6.0–7.0	6.5	0.8195	0.3636 ·	0.2980	1.9371
7.0–8.0	7.5	0.9090	0.3333	0.3030	2.2727
8.0–9.0	8.5	0.8761	0.2000	0.1752	1.4893
9.0–10.0	9.5	0.6833	0.2000	0.1366	1.2984

$$R_0 = \sum_0^\infty l_x b_x = 2.7999 \qquad \sum_0^\infty V_x x = 14.9371$$

Age-specific fertility (b_x) is considered to be the average number of offspring of the same sex as the parent, in our case female, that are expected from an animal in an age class (x to x+1) (Krebs, 1985). In this study, the age classes and time periods used are intervals of one year. The greatest fertility is achieved at different ages for each species, Cuvier's at three years old and Dama and Dorcas at five and six years old respectively.

There are several related demographic parameters that let us predict how a population will behave. There are indicators of the population's capacity for change (Foose, 1980). The net reproductive rates (R_0) is the sum of the product of the survivals and fertilities per age class, $R_0 = $ all ages/$\Sigma l_x \cdot b_x$. Hence, R_0 is a measure of the total number of offspring an animal would be expected to produce if it survived through its maximum lifespan. A related parameter is the annual rate of change (λ), which can be defined as R_0 1/G. A third parameter measuring a population's capacity for change under some constant schedule of survival and fertility is the intrinsic rate of change (R_m). It is related to λ by $R_m = L_n\lambda$.

In the three cases studied, predictions produced by R_0 (> 1), λ (1) and R_m (> 0) (Table 20.5) indicate that our populations of Gazelle

Table 20.5: Fertility and demographic parameters for G. *dama*, G. *cuvieri* and G. *dorcas* (R_0 = net reproductive rate, G = Length of a generation, λ = annual rate of change, R_m = intrinsic rate of change)

	R_0	G	λ	R_m
G. *dama*	2.80	5.25	1.22	0.20
G. *cuvieri*	3.81	3.3	1.5	0.41
G. *dorcas*	2.45	4.67	1.21	0.19

will prosper in the forthcoming years. Indeed the projections for these species are representative of many captive populations (Foose, 1980; Beck and Wemmer, 1983), which possess the potential to expand rapidly or explode beyond the carrying capacity of zoos, a development that is both a tribute and a tribulation for captive husbandry. Fertility parameters in Cuvier's Gazelle show a faster growing capacity than the other species and this is due to the twins-partum occurrence. The low survival rate, however, as mentioned earlier, prevents quick progress.

The mean length of a generation (G) is the mean period elapsing between the birth of parents and the birth of offspring. Obviously, this is only an approximate definition, since offspring are born over a period of time and not all at once. The mean length of a generation is defined approximately as $G = (\Sigma l_x.b_x.x)/(l_x.b_x)$. All of the gazelle species, especially Cuvier's, showed a very short generation time. Values computed for Przewalski Horses, Okapi and Gaur, by comparison (Table 20.6), show a lower capacity for growth than do our populations.

According to Read and Harvey (1986), captive-propagation plans should aim to start with more than 20 founders (although the numbers depend on the rate of growth and generation time), to

Table 20.6: Demographic and fertility parameters in females of other species in captivity

	R_0	λ	R_m	G
Przewalski Horse	2.067	1.068	0.066	12 (Foose 1980)
Gaur	2.433	1.111	0.105	8.5 (Foose 1980)
Okapi	1.175	1.017	0.017	9.5 (Foose 1980)
Père David's Deer		0.984		(Foose and Foose 1983)

increase population size in a few generations so that the effects of genetic drift are minimised, and to ensure survival of the species in captivity. Then, reproduction should be delayed artificially. Our founder-population numbers are not very high but our objectives are to get a big population of each species as soon as possible in order to produce a surplus of animals for re-introduction projects. Once achieved, we shall continue with a progressive reduction in reproduction until we get a stable population, in order to avoid dangerous distortions in the age and sex structures. Whatever the method used, the selection of particular animals for removal or for breeding should be based on genetic criteria with the aim of maximising effective population size and minimising closely related reproduction. All of these objectives must be achieved in co-operation with as many institutions as possible.

References

Alados, C.L. (1987) A cladistic approach to the taxonomy of the Dorcas gazelles. *Israel Journal of Zoology*.

Ansell, W.F.M. (1971) Order Artiodactyla. In Meester, J., and Setzer, H.W. (eds), *The Mammals of Africa: An identification manual*. Smithsonian Institution Press, Washington D.C.: pp. 1–84.

Aulagnier, S., and Thevenot M. (in prep.) *Catalogue des Mammifères Sauvages du Maroc*.

Beck, B.B., and Wemmer, C. (1983) *The Biology and Management of an Extinct Species: Père David's Deer*. Noyes Publications, Park Ridge, New Jersey.

Benirschke, K. (1985) The genetic management of exotic animals. *Symp. Zool. Soc. Lond.* 54: 71–87.

Boroviczeny, I. (1981) In *Red Data Book* series (in press).

Caughley, G. (1977) *Analysis of Vertebrate Populations*. John Wiley and Sons, Chichester.

Chapuis, M. (1961) Evolution and protection of the wildlife of Morocco. *African Wildlife 15* (2): 107–12.

Chiang, C.L. (1984) *The Life Table and Its Applications*. R.E. Krieger and Co., Mabar, Florida.

Escos, J. (in press) *Gazella cuvieri* Studbook. Servicio de Publicaciones de C.S.I.C., Spain.

Escos, J., and Gomendio, M. (1984) Effects of changes in the social environment of captive *Gazella cuvieri* groups. Ungulate Research Group Meeting, London, 1984 (unpubl.).

Foose, T.J. (1980) Demographic management of endangered species in captivity. *Int. Zoo Ybk 20*: 154–66.

Captive Populations of Antilopinae and Caprinae

Foose, T.J., and Foose, E. (1983) Demographic and genetic status and management. In Beck, B.B., and Wemmer, C. (eds), *The Biology and Management of an Extinct Species: Père David's Deer*. Noyes Publications, New Jersey: pp. 133–81.

Gillet, H. (1969) L'oryx gazelle et l'addax. Distribution géographique. Chances de survie. *C.R. Biogéogr. 405*: 117–89.

Gomendio, M., and Escos, J. (1984) Dominance relationships among *Gazella cuvieri* adult females. Ungulate Research Group Meeting, London, 1984 (unpubl.).

Grettenberger, J.F., and Newby, J.E. (1985) The status and ecology of the Dama gazelle in the Air and Tenere National Nature Reserve, Niger. *Biological Conservation 38*: 207–16.

Groves, C.P. (1981) Notes on the Dorcas gazelles of North Africa. *Annali Mus. Cic. St. Nat. G. Doria 83*: 455–71.

Harper, F. (1945) *Extinct and Vanishing Mammals of the Old World*. American Committee for International Wild Life Preservation, New York.

Keay, R.W.S. (1959) *Vegetation Map of Africa South of the Tropic of Cancer*. Oxford University Press, Oxford.

Keyfitz (1977) *Introduction to the Mathematics of Populations*. Addison-Wesley, Reading, Massachusetts.

Krebs, C.J. (1985) *Ecology: The Experimental Analysis of Distribution and Abundance*. 3rd Ed., Wilson, C.M., and Detgan, H. (eds). Harper and Row, New York.

Newby, J.E. (1981a) Is this the last chance for North Africa's fauna? *World Wildlife Fund Monthly Report*, June. Project 1624. Antelopes Sahelo-Saharan: 135–42.

Newby, J.E. (1981b) The conservation status of the Sahelo-Saharan fauna of Africa. Unpublished Report: pp. 18.

Panouse, J.B. (1957) Les mammifères du Maroc. *Trav. Inst. Sci. Cherifien (Ser. Zool.) 5*: 1–206.

Read, A.F., and Harvey, P.M. (1986) Genetic management in zoos. *Nature 322*: 308–410.

Red Data Book (in press) Vol. 1, Mammalia. IUCN, Gland, Switzerland.

Valverde, J. (1968) Ecological bases for fauna conservation in Western Sahara. *Proc. IBT/CT Tech. Meeting*, Cons. Nat., Hammamet.

Willan, R.G.M. (1973) Tunisia's wildlife. *Oryx 12* (1): 74–6.

21. Research and Management of Arabian Sand Gazelle in the USA

Steven C. Kingswood and Arlene T. Kumamoto

Abstract

Wild populations of Arabian Sand Gazelle *Gazella subgutturosa marica* have been greatly reduced since the early 1900s owing to mechanised hunting. Current populations may number only a few thousand and are vulnerable throughout the Sand Gazelle's range. A captive population in the USA is an important element in the conservation of this desert gazelle. Chromosome analysis (karyotyping) of captive Sand Gazelles was initiated to aid correct identification of these animals and has revealed chromosomal differences from the Arabian Gazelle *Gazella gazella arabica* and the Persian Gazelle *Gazella subgutturosa subgutturosa*. These karyotypic differences support phenotypic and morphometric differences between the two taxa. Further study utilising such techniques as electrophoresis and mitochondrial DNA analysis should help shed light on the systematics of this group. This information will clearly have direct application to such captive-management considerations as reproductive fitness. Perhaps more important for long-term conservation planning will be additional scientific criteria aiding identification of conservation priorities.

Introduction

'The Arabian Oryx may now be extinct in the wild. If so it was exterminated by hunters in four-wheel drive vehicles using automatic weapons' (Jungius, 1978). Anticipation of this event inspired and prompted formation of the World Herd in 1962. Conservationists from around the world have been brought together in London in 1987 to celebrate the continued existence of Arabian Oryx, particularly where it naturally belongs, but the Oryx is not the only species of the Arabian Peninsula to suffer at the hands of man. All three native species of gazelle, the Mountain Gazelle *Gazella gazella*,

Sand Gazelle *G. subgutturosa marica* and Saudi Gazelle *G. (dorcas) saudiya*, have been greatly reduced since the First World War by mechanised hunting. Currently, IUCN recognises the Mountain Gazelle as 'vulnerable', while the Sand Gazelle is considered 'endangered' (Anon., 1986). Obviously, conservation of these animals must involve proper management of habitat and protection from excessive hunting. Ryder (in press) has recently described the urgent need for intervention to prevent the extinction of local populations and subspecies of a number of endangered gazelle species and, as has been shown with Arabian Oryx, captive management is an important means of preserving endangered species. This paper will focus on efforts in the USA to preserve the Sand Gazelle through captive breeding and systematics research. The results of this present study can serve as a model for other taxa in need of conservation.

The Goitred Gazelle *Gazella subgutturosa* is found in desert and sub-desert steppes from northern China to the Arabian Peninsula (Nowak and Paradiso, 1983). In the Middle East, two forms are recognised. The nominate form, *G. s. subgutturosa*, is found from the Soviet Union to the Arabian Peninsula. *G. s. marica*, known as the Arabian Sand Gazelle, occurs from eastern Jordan south throughout the sand deserts, limestone plateau and gravel plains of the Arabian Peninsula (Harrison, 1968). Groves (1985) also recognises *G. s. yarkandensis* and *G. s. hillieriana* from China and Mongolia.

Throughout its range, the Goitred Gazelle's population is being reduced. It is regarded as vulnerable in China, declining in Mongolia and Pakistan, and almost extinct in Afghanistan (Nogge, 1974; Anon., 1981; Wang, 1982 *in litt.*; Tsertgmid and Dashdorj, 1984). The major threat to the Sand Gazelle is hunting, although in some areas over-grazing by domestic livestock, especially goats, is a problem. The Sand Gazelle has been hunted since the existence of Stone Age man. More recently, 'desert kites' (large triangular-shaped corrals built from stones) were used by bedouin groups to trap as many as several hundred Sand Gazelles (Mendelssohn, 1974). It was not until the period following World War I, however, that hunting played a significant role in the decline of the species when the construction of roads and the increased availability of four-wheel-drive vehicles and automatic weapons opened up much of the rugged wilderness previously inaccessible to man. The current wild population is conservatively estimated to be a few thousand, but more accurate census data are needed (Williamson, 1987).

Sand Gazelles are held at three US Zoos: San Antonio, Sedgwick County (Wichita, Kansas) and San Diego Wild Animal Park. This captive population, numbering 22:32 to date, originated primarily from 4:4 animals sent to San Antonio Zoo in 1965 by HM King Hussein of Jordan. A few years later, Busch Gardens in Tampa, Florida, imported 0:2 from The Federal Republic of Germany. All of these original imports were initially identified as Arabian Gazelle *G. gazella arabica*. In 1974, the original identification of San Antonio Zoo stock was questioned by the Zoo's staff after comparing photos of Arabian Gazelle at Chester, United Kingdom. With the help of gazelle behaviourist Dr E.C. Mungall, the animals were re-identified as Sand Gazelles (Reed, *in litt.*). Phenotypically, these animals conform to the characteristics of Sand Gazelle as outlined by Groves (1969) and Harrison (1968). The distinctions between various gazelle taxa from the Arabian Peninsula, however, are often slight, with apparent intergradation.

Compounding the identification problem is the fact that the precise origin of the captive population is unknown. Although the majority of Sand Gazelle in the USA are derived from Jordanian stock, it is uncertain whether the animals were captive and maintained in pure species or subspecies groups before importation to the US. Even if they were known to be wild-caught in Jordan, natural hybridisation could occur as this is a possible zone of intergradation between Persian Gazelle and Sand Gazelle (Figure 21.1). Further assistance with this identification problem was sought from Dr O.A. Ryder of San Diego Zoo, CRES. At his suggestion, a cytogenetic study of Sand Gazelles was initiated to determine whether species and subspecies identification could be delineated by chromosomal analysis.

Materials and Methods

Heparinised whole blood and skin biopsy samples were transported at ambient temperatures to the CRES Cytogenetics Laboratory within one day of sampling. Lymphocytes were cultured following the method of Arakaki and Sparkes (1963), using pokeweed as mitogenic stimulant. Primary tissue cultures were initiated from the skin biopsies and followed methods described previously (Kumamoto and Bogart, 1984). Harvest of mitotic cells followed that of Yu *et al.* (1981). Slide preparation and Giemsa-banding

Figure 21.1: Range of Sand and Persian Gazelle in the Middle East based on Groves (1969) and Harrison (1968). Note the range overlap of the two forms. This is an area of possible phenotypic and genotypic intergradation. Sand Gazelle populations have been reduced by hunting and recent reports of sightings from Williamson (1987) are indicated

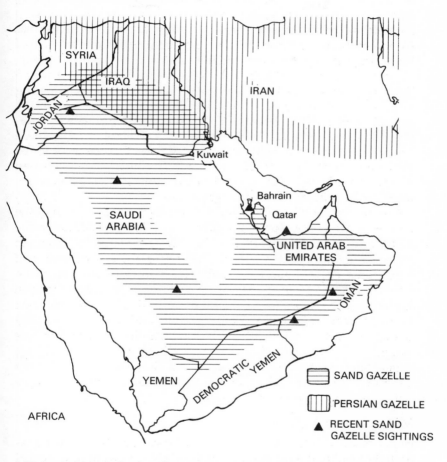

followed the methods of Franke and Oliver (1978) and Seabright (1972) respectively.

Samples were as follows:

Arabian Gazelle (*Gazella gazella arabica*) – Samples from one male and three females were obtained from Marwell Zoological Park, United Kingdom.

215

Sand Gazelle (*Gazella subgutturosa marica*) – 38 male and 33 female specimens were analysed. Specimens were received from the following institutions: San Antonio Zoo, Texas; Sedgwick County, Wichita, Kansas; Busch Gardens, Tampa, Florida; San Diego Wild Animal Park, California.

Persian Gazelle (*Gazella subgutturosa subgutturosa*) – five males and four females were evaluated. All specimens were from the San Diego/Wild Animal Park collection.

Results

The diploid number in Sand Gazelle males was found to be 2n=31, 32 or 33, while in females 2n=30, 31 or 32 (Table 21.1). Males have one more chromosome owing to a translocation of an acrocentric autosome onto the X sex chromosome. G-band analysis identifies the extra 'unpaired' autosome to be homologous with the distal portion of the X chromosome. This compound X sex chromosome mechanism has been described in other gazelle species (Effron *et al.*, 1976; Benirschke *et al.*, 1984; Benirschke, 1985). The range in diploid number in this group of animals, however, is caused by a centric fusion polymorphism which is manifested in both homozygous and heterozygous forms. One form, represented by males 2n=33, females 2n=32, has two pairs of acrocentric chromosomes, //14 //15 (Figure 21.2.).

Table 21.1: Diploid number in Sand Gazelle and number of specimens evaluated

	Males	Females
Arabian Gazelle *G. gazella arabica*	2N=35 (1)	2N=34 (3)
Persian Gazelle *G. subgutturosa subgutturosa*	2N=31 (5)	2N=30 (4)
Sand Gazelle *G. subgutturosa marica*	2N=31 (18) 2N=32 (19) 2N=33 (1)	2N=30 (10) 2N=31 (12) 2N=32 (11)

In the second form (Figure 21.3), represented by males 2n=31, females 2n=30, there is a fusion of the two acrocentric pairs //14 and //15 to form a large metacentric pair. The heterozygous form is represented by males 2n=32, females 2n-31 (Figure 21.4). There seems to be no correlation between karyotype and phenotype as the phenotype seems relatively consistent, regardless of karyotype.

Figure 21.2: G-banded karyotype of female *G.s. marica* 2n=32. Note two pairs of acrocentric autosome No. 14 and No. 15

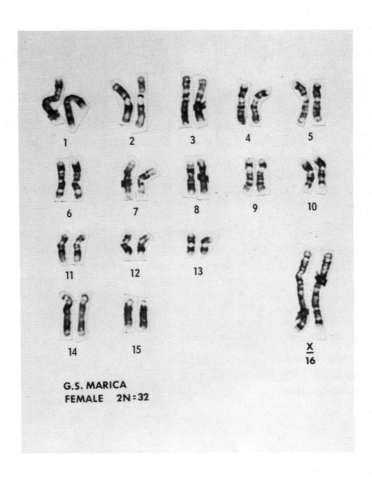

Figure 21.3: G-banded karyotype of female *G.s. marica* 2n=30. This karyotype depicts the large metacentric pair of chromosome [14/15] formed by the centric fusion of acrocentric autosome pairs Nos. 14 and 15. This form is homozygous for the fusion

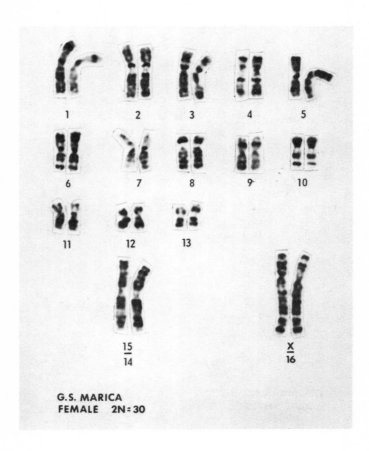

Figure 21.4: G-banded karyotype of male *G.s. marica* 2n=32. Heterozygous form of the autosome centric fusion. This animal has inherited one fused chromosome and one each of the matching acrocentric chromosomes (//14 and //15). Note also the translocation of autosome //16 onto the end of the X sex chromosome, resulting in the extra 'unpaired' //16 in the male form. Females inherit two X chromosomes, both with the autosome –X fusion, and therefore do not have an extra unpaired element

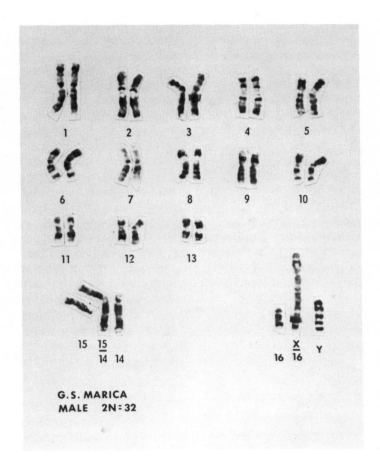

G.S. MARICA
MALE 2N = 32

In order to attempt to trace the transmission of the centric Robertsonian fusion, a registry is being compiled so that a pedigree can be maintained. By karyotyping the individuals of successive generations, this fusion can be studied and any reproductive consequences resulting from different karyotype pairings can be documented. Results to date do not indicate that the crossing of different cytotypes impairs overall reproduction. Both male and female of the heterozygous form are fertile and produce offspring when crossed to any of the three cytotypes (Figure 21.5). Attempts to pair males and females of the same type (i.e. 2n=31 males with 2n=30 females, and 2n=33 males with 2n=32 females) will be made in the future, in an attempt to document whether breeding efficacy and infant survival is affected.

Karyotypes of Arabian Gazelle revealed diploid numbers of 2n=35 for the male and 2n=34 for female (confirming a previously published report by Wahrman *et al.*, 1973) (Figure 21.6). As in the Sand Gazelle, there is an autosome-X chromosome translocation accounting for the difference in diploid number between males and females.

Figure 21.5: Partial pedigree of captive Sand Gazelle with diploid numbers

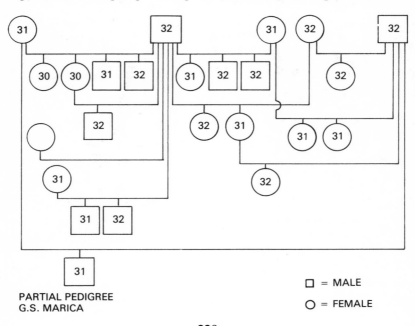

PARTIAL PEDIGREE
G.S. MARICA

□ = MALE
○ = FEMALE

220

Figure 21.6: G-banded karyotype of male *G.g. arabica* 2n=35. Similarities exist between G-banded karyotypes of all members of the gazelle genus (Effron *et al.*, 1976), Sand and Arabian Gazelles included. The basic karyotype between these two species is, however, very different. Note autosomal pairs //15, 16 and 17 which are lacking in the Sand Gazelle karyotypes (Figures 21.1, 21.2, 21.3). The Y chromosome of the Arabian Gazelle has a different G-banding pattern from that in the Sand Gazelle

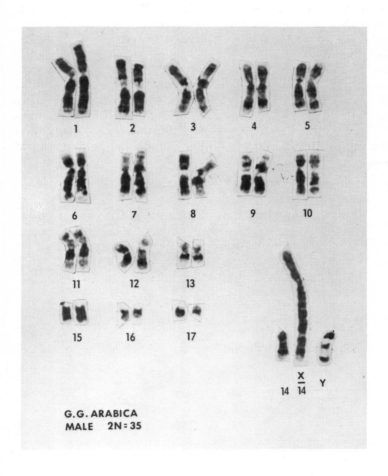

G.G. ARABICA
MALE 2N = 35

While there are similarities between G-banded karyotypes of Sand and Arabian Gazelles, and comparisons can be drawn, the basic karyotype differs between the two in number and morphology. The Arabian Gazelle has three pairs of acrocentric chromosomes not found in any of the Sand Gazelle forms. Because of these evident differences we can conclude that the animals in the US collections identified as Sand Gazelle originating from the two importations during the 1960s are *G.s. marica* and not *G.g. arabica* or hybrids thereof.

Analysis of the Persian Gazelle samples indicated a consistent diploid number of $2n=31$ in males and $2n=30$ in females, verifying previously published chromosomal descriptions of this species (Wurster, 1972; Effron *et al.*, 1976). In comparison with Sand Gazelle, the karyotypes of Persian Gazelle are identical to those of the fusion homozygous Sand Gazelle karyotype $2n=31$ males/30 females. There is exact homology of G-banding patterns in all pairs of a male Persian Gazelle ($2n=31$) and a male Sand Gazelle ($2n=31$). Phenotypically the two subspecies are distinguishable, with Sand Gazelle being smaller and more rotund, light in colour, having a white face and females with well-developed horns.

The founder stock (1:2) of the San Diego Persian Gazelle analysed in this study were received in the 1960s from the Tehran Zoo, Iran. Historical information regarding these animals is lacking. It is not known whether these animals were wild-caught or captive-bred, nor the locality in the wild where they or their founders were taken. If it is assumed that these animals were taken from the local Iranian gazelle population, then these animals would represent true Persian Gazelle, since this is an area removed from the zone of known overlap between the two subspecies.

With these data we can therefore still not specifically rule out the possibility that the US population that we are calling Sand Gazelle may be a genetically mixed group of Persian and Sand Gazelles, although phenotypically these animals conform to the characteristics of Sand Gazelle as described in the literature (Harrison, 1968; Groves, 1969). Sampling of Sand Gazelle from territories outside the areas of mixed population with Persian Gazelle would greatly aid in clarifying phenotypic identification as well as the cytogenetics of this subspecies.

It is of interest to note that, while both the Sand Gazelle and the Persian Gazelle populations at the San Diego Wild Animal Park started from small founder populations in the 1960s, there is a difference in breeding record. There has been a total of 418 births in the Persian Gazelle population, while in the Sand Gazelle it has been just under half that number, with 206 births. There also seems to be better infant survival in the Persian Gazelle than in the Sand Gazelle, but documentation of this has yet to be done. The overall reduced reproduction rate in the Sand Gazelle (as compared with the Persian Gazelle) could very well be a reflection of the chromosomal polymorphism in this group. Unfortunately, little can be said regarding the effects of inbreeding depression in the Sand Gazelle since pedigree data of early generations are lacking and numerous uncertainties of family relationships must exist in the present captive population. Accurate breeding records are sometimes difficult to keep with animals in herd situations, but this information is essential in order to assess accurately genetic parameters which affect reproduction.

Discussion

Cross-breeding of chromosomally distinct taxa often results in subfertility of hybrids, perinatal mortality and abortions, or even sterility. In Soemmerring's Gazelle *Gazella soemmerringi*, numerous chromosome fusions were found to lead to reproductive problems (Benirschke *et al.*, 1984). The confusing relationships and the vast distribution of the genus *Gazella* prompted Blandford (1873) to conclude that this group has recently gone through a period of rapid expansion. This seeming ease of hybridisation among the gazelles and their relatives may be another consequence of rapid expansion with little evolutionary time for genotypic and phenotypic differentiation or for the development of reproductive-isolating mechanisms (Mungall, *in litt.*).

Monitoring the reproductive consequences of karyotypic variation in Sand Gazelle must be continued for a better understanding of its significance. The structural polymorphism described in this paper does not seem to affect captive Sand Gazelle fertility, but more data need to be gathered relating specifically to possible effects on perinatal mortality and reduced survival. To document properly the effects of this polymorphism on fitness, the segregation of the alternative cytotypes resulting from different crosses must be tracked in order to detect any trends or bias in cytotype of those animals surviving versus those not surviving. It is, therefore, important to obtain post-mortem samples since valuable information may be obtained from these samples.

Information on populations in the wild, particularly karyotypes of Sand Gazelle farther south on the Arabian Peninsula and away from the area of possible range overlap with the Persian Gazelle, would be extremely valuable. Lacking information regarding the precise origin of US Sand Gazelle illustrates the importance of documenting capture or sampling locations for future studies. All captive specimens should be karyotyped for genotypic evaluation and photographed for phenotypic documentation. Multivariate analysis of morphometric characters indicates morphological differences between Sand and Persian Gazelles (Groves, 1969). Deceased specimens are important for further morphometric study, and frozen tissue samples for mitochondrial DNA analysis. Individual identification and pedigrees of all breeding are extremely important. Karyotyping has illustrated genetic differences among Sand Gazelle that may be important in answering systematic questions. Application of such techniques as electrophoresis and mitochondrial DNA analysis should help shed light on the systematics of this group. Mitochondrial DNA has a rapid rate of evolution in comparison with the rates of change in nuclear genes (Brown *et al.*, 1979) and has been used therefore to investigate phylogenetic and systematic relationships between related taxa with recent times of divergence (Avise *et al.*, 1979; Brown *et al.*, 1979; Brown and Simpson, 1981; George and Ryder, 1986). Perhaps more important for long-term conservation planning will be additional scientific criteria aiding identification of conservation priorities. If one goal of exotic-animal conservation programmes is the preservation of genetic diversity, then every attempt should be made to define that diversity, particularly in founding captive populations.

Acknowledgements

We thank K.C. Fletcher, W. Bryant, J. Oosterhuis, J. Olsen and J.M. Knowles for blood and skin samples; also L.E. Killmar and G.S. Lentz for additional project support. K. Benirschke and O.A. Ryder provided valuable counsel and reviewed the manuscript. Manuscript presentation was greatly aided by A.E. Vincent, J. Fleshman, R. Faren, R.L. Smith and M. Graves, and special thanks go to M.C. Reed for the initiation of this project, support and encouragement along the way.

Arabian Sand Gazelle in the USA

References

Anonymous (1981) Proposal to include *Gazella subgutturosa* in Appendix I of the Convention on International Trade in Endangered Species of Wild Fauna and Flora. Proponent: Islamic Republic of Pakistan.

Anonymous (1986) *1986 IUCN Red List of Threatened Animals*. IUCN Conservation Monitoring Centre, Cambridge, United Kingdom.

Arakaki, D.T., and Sparkes, R.S. (1963) Leukocyte chromosomes from culture of whole blood. *Cytogenetics* 2: 57–60.

Avise, J.C., Lansman, R.A., and Shade, R.O. (1979) The use of restriction endonucleases to measure mitochondrial DNA sequence relatedness in natural populations. I. Population structure and evolution in the genus *Peromyscus*. *Genetics* 92: 279–95.

Benirschke, K. (1985) The genetic management of exotic species. In Hearn, J.P., and Hodges, J.K. (eds), *Advances in Animal Conservation*. Zoological Society of London Symposium 54, Clarendon Press: pp. 71–87.

Benirschke, K., Kumamoto, A.T., Olsen, J.H., Williams, M.M., and Oosterhuis, J. (1984) On the chromosomes of *Gazella soemmerringi* Cretzschmar, 1926. *Z. Säugetierk.* 49: 368–73.

Blandford, W.T. (1873) On the gazelles of India and Persia. Proceedings of the Zoological Society of London.

Brown, W.M., George Jr., M., and Wilson, A.C. (1979) Rapid evolution of animal mitochondrial DNA. *Proc. Nat. Acad. Sci.* USA 77: 3605–9.

Brown, G.G., and Simpson, M.V. (1981) Intra and interspecific variation of the mitochondrial genome in *Rattus norvegicus* and *Rattus rattus*: Restriction enzyme analysis of variant mitochondrial DNA molecules and their evolutionary relationships. *Genetics* 97: 125–43.

Effron, M., Bogart, M.H., Kumamoto, A.T., and Benirschke, K. (1976) Chromosome studies in the mammalian subfamily Antilopinae. *Genetica* 46: 419–44.

Franke, U., and Oliver, N. (1978) Quantitative analysis of high resolution trypsin-Giemsa bands on human prometaphase chromosomes. *Human Genetics* 45: 137–65.

George Jr., M., and Ryder, O.A. (1986) Mitochrondrial DNA evolution in the genus *Equus*. *Mol. Bio. Evol.* 3 (6): 535–46.

Groves, C.P. (1969) On the smaller gazelles of the genus *Gazella* de Blainville, 1816. *Z. Säugetierk.* 34: 38–60.

Groves, C.P. (1985) An introduction to the gazelles. Chinkara: Bulletin of Gazelle Research Group 1 (1): 4–16.

Harrison, D.L. (1968) *The Mammals of Arabia*, Vol. 2, Carnivora, Hyracoidea, Artiodactyla. Ernest Benn, London.

Jungius, H. (1978) Plan to restore Arabian oryx in Oman. *Oryx* 14 (4): 328–36.

Kumamoto, A.T., and Bogart, N.H. (1984) The chromosomes of Cuvier's Gazelle. In Ryder, O.A., and Byrd (eds), *One Medicine – A Tribute to*

Kurt Benirschke. Spring-Verlag: pp. 101–8.

Mendelssohn, H. (1974) The development of the populations of gazelles in Israel and their behavioural adaptations. In Geist, V., and Walther, F. (eds), *The Behaviour of Ungulates and its Relation to Management*, Vol. 2. IUCN Publications, New Series, No. 24, IUCN, Switzerland.

Nogge, G. (1974) Kabul Zoo. *Int. Zoo News 21* (1): 7–9.

Nowak, R.M., and Paradiso, J.L. (eds) (1983) *Walker's Mammals of the World*, 4th Ed. John Hopkins University Press, Baltimore and London.

Ryder, O.A. (1987) Conservation action for gazelles: an urgent need. *Trends in Ecology Evolution* (in press).

Seabright, M. (1972) The use of proteolytic enzymes for the mapping of structural rearrangements in the chromosomes of man. *Chromsoma 36*: 204–10.

Tsertgmid, D., and Dashdorj, A. (1984) Wild horses and other endangered wildlife in Mongolia. *Oryx 12* (3): 361–70.

Wahrman,| J., Richler,| C., Goitein, R., Horowitz, A., and Mendelssohn, H. (1973) Abstract: Multiple sex chromosome evolution, hybridization and differential X chromosome inactivation in gazelles. *Chrom. Today 4*: 434.

Williamson, J.E. (1987) Draft 8 of Arabian sand gazelle data sheet. IUCN Conservation Monitoring Centre, Cambridge, United Kingdom.

Wurster, D.H. (1972) Sex chromosome translocations and karyotypes in bovidae tribes. *Cytogenetics 11*: 197–207.

Yu, R.L., Aronson, M.M., and Nichols, W.W. (1981) High resolution bands in human fibroblast chromosomes induced by actinomycin D. *Cytogenet.Cell Genet. 31*: 111–14.

22. Artificial Insemination of Addax with Thawed Frozen Semen

Mary A. Densmore and Duane C. Kraemer

Introduction

Artificial insemination (AI) is one method currently being refined for use in zoo animals which would provide a means of optimising reproduction in rare and endangered species. Semen preservation and shipment for AI, if perfected, would be helpful in controlling inbreeding and in reducing the need to transport animals for breeding purposes. In addition, semen from wild males could be used to breed females in captivity without removing the males from their normal habitat.

This work was part of a research project on the reproductive biology of Addax *Addax nasomaculatus* in captivity. Specific objectives were to:

1. Obtain data on the quality of Addax semen.
2. Investigate methods of preserving Addax semen.
3. Develop a method for regulating ovulation in Addax.
4. Develop a feasible method for AI of Addax.

Further details and results of the research project have been or will be published (Densmore and Kraemer, 1986; Densmore *et al.*, 1987a, 1987b, 1987c).

Animals

All of the Addax used in these studies were mother-raised. The date and place of birth of each Addax are given in Table 22.1 below.

Diet consisted of coastal Bermuda grass hay, water and salt/ mineral block available *ad libitum*, supplemented daily by 0.1 – 0.5 kg 14% protein feed (males) or 0.1 – 1.0 kg 16% protein feed

Table 22.1: The date of birth and place of birth of the Addax used in this project

ID	Sex	Date of Birth	Place of Birth
M1	M	December 1973 ± 4 m	San Diego Wild Animal Park
M2	M	25 April 1975	Camp Cooley Ranch
M3	M	18 March 1976	Camp Cooley Ranch
M4	M	30 July 1978	Camp Cooley Ranch
F2	F	20 October 1980	Camp Cooley Ranch
F3	F	Febuary/March 1980	Camp Cooley Ranch

(females). All animals were in good body condition and showed no clinical signs of disease during the studies. The male Addax were housed at a private facility 11 kilometres from Texas A & M University. The female Addax were housed at Texas A & M Univerity through June 1984, and at a private facility 81 kilometres from Texas A & M University after June 1984.

Semen Collection

Semen was collected every four weeks for one year (13 collections), beginning on 23 June 1980. Immobilisation was achieved using a combination of 3–4 milligrams etorphine hydrochloride (M99; Lemmon Co., Sellersville, Pennsylvania, USA) and 8–10 milligrams xylazine hydrochloride (Rompun; Haver Lockhart, Shawnee, Kansas, USA). The length of immobilisation ranged from 17 to 122 minutes (mean 35.4 minutes). Reversal was accomplished by IV injection of an appropriate volume of diprenorphine hydrochloride (M5050; Lemmon Co., Sellersville, Pennsylvania, USA).

Semen was collected from the immobilised males by electroejaculation using a portable transistorised ejaculator (Mode S25; Standard Precision Electronics, Denver, Colorado, USA) with a ram probe. Semen was obtained from the male Addax on 50 of the 52 scheduled attempts. Seven ejaculates contained urine and one was clear. The remaining semen samples collected were milky-white in colour and had a viscosity of 1 on a scale of 1 (watery) to 4 (highly viscous). The status of sperm movement was 5 on a scale of 0 (no movement) to 5 (fast forward progression) in all of the samples which were checked immediately after collection. Volume of the ejaculates ranged from 0.3 – 4.2 ml (mean 1.57 ± 0.88 ml).

Mean osmolarity of five semen samples was 299.8 mOsm/L. The overall mean, standard deviation (SD) and range of four other semen variables and scrotal diameter and volume are presented in Table 22.2.

Table 22.2: Reproductive data from four immobilised Addax during the period June 1980 – May 1981

Parameter	n	Range	Mean±SD
Total Number of Sperm	45	$17.7–3095.5 \times 10^6$	$704.6 \pm 745.6 \times 10^6$
Normal Sperm	45	4–89%	$60.0 \pm 20.7\%$
Immature Sperm	45	0–61%	$5.2 \pm 13.3\%$
Semen pH	11	6.2–7.0	6.74 ± 0.25
Scrotal Diameter	51	5.4–7.0 cm	6.57 ± 4.24cm
Scrotal Volume	51	130–265 cm^3	204.6 ± 34.4cm^3

Scrotal volume and scrotal diameter were calculated from the measured length and circumference of the scrotum. Four of the parameters varied significantly between males and statistics for each male for these parameters are given in Table 22.3.

Semen Preservation

The semen samples used in this study were obtained during the semen-collection study. Each sample was diluted within five minutes of collection with one of the extenders listed in Table 22.4. When the tris or raffinose extenders were used, the non-glycerolated portion was added in the first dilution and the portion containing glycerol was added in the second dilution.

The extended samples were then placed in an ice chest until they could be transported to Texas A & M University (0.5–3.5 hours). After equilibration in a cold room (4°C) for 20–30 minutes, the samples were diluted with a volume of diluent equal to the volume of diluent added at the first dilution, gently mixed and equilibrated for an additional 20–30 minutes at 4°C. The final dilution ratio was normally 1:3 (semen:final volume). The diluted semen was then frozen either as pellets or in 0.25-ml straws. If frozen as pellets, the diluted semen was dropped onto dry ice (-79°C) and equilibrated for three minutes. The pellets were then plunged into liquid nitrogen and stored at -196°C in plastic screw-top vials. If frozen in straws, the loaded sealed straws were either placed between two blocks of dry ice for three minutes or frozen in liquid nitrogen vapor and then plunged into liquid nitrogen. Straws were thawed in a 37°C water bath. Pellets were thawed in 0.9% NaCl (37°C).

Table 22.3: Statistics and results of Duncan's Multiple Range Test on the means for reproductive parameters which varied significantly between four male Addax

Parameter	Male	n	Range	Mean ± SD	Duncan's Grouping[a]
Normal	M1	11	46–89%	69.4±14.0%	A
Sperm	M2	12	56–87%	75.2±10.8%	A
	M3	10	27–73%	49.1±16.2%	B
	M4	12	4–72%	45.2±22.9%	B
Immature	M1	11	0–1%	0.4±0.5%	B
Sperm	M2	12	0–5%	0.8±1.6%	B
	M3	10	0–4%	1.0±1.3%	B
	M4	12	0–61%	17.4±21.8%	A
Scrotal	M1	13	5.8–7.0 cm	6.50±0.3 cm	B
Diameter	M2	13	5.7–6.5 cm	6.23±0.25 cm	C
	M3	12	6.7–7.0 cm	6.75±0.16 cm	A
	M4	13	5.4–6.5 cm	5.96±0.47 cm	D
Scrotal	M1	13	176–246 cm^3	217.4±24.6 cm^3	A,B
Volume	M2	13	155-244 cm^3	198.4±23.5 cm^3	B
	M3	12	202–265 cm^3	234.6±20.4 cm^3	A
	M4	13	130–223 cm^3	170.5±31.8 cm^3	C

Note: a. Within each parameter, means with the same letter did not vary significantly (r = 0.05).

The ability of each of three extenders to protect Addax sperm during freezing and thawing was evaluated *in vitro* using a bovine cervical mucus penetration test (Syva Penetrak Test; Syva Inc., Palo Alto, California, USA). Fifteen semen samples were selected and tested on the basis of high post-thaw percent motility (subjective) (Table 22.5). Sperm frozen in the raffinose extender migrated significantly shorter distances (10.5–18.0 mm, mean 14.6 mm) than sperm frozen in either the tris (22.0–39.5 mm, mean 30.4 mm) or lactose (22.5–37.5 mm, mean 27.6 mm) extenders. The post-thaw motility of semen samples and the maximum distance travelled by sperm from those samples were significantly correlated (r=0.52, p=0.04).

Table 22.4: Ingredients of the three semen extenders tested

Lactose Extender
11 g Lactose
20 ml egg yolk
4ml Glycerol
500,000 U Penicillin
100 mg Streptomycin sulfate
QS to 100 ml with distilled water

Tris Extender
3.2028 g Tris (hydroxymethyl) aminomethane
1.676 g Citric Acid
20 ml egg yolk
10 ml Antibiotic-antimycotic mixture[a]
7 ml Glycerol[b]
QS to 100 ml with distilled water

Raffinose Extender
18.5 g Raffinose
20 ml egg yolk
10 ml Antibiotic-antimycotic mixture[a]
4.7 ml Glycerol[b]
QS to 100 ml with distilled water

Notes: a. Gibco, Grand Island, New York (cat. 600–5204)
b. Glycerol added to glycerolated portion only.

Ovulation Regulation

Two oestrus control regimens were tested. The female Addax were manually restrained without tranquilisers or immobilising drugs during all procedures.

Regimen No. 1: Prostaglandin (cloprostenol sodium; 125 micrograms, IM) and Pregnant Mares' Serum Gonadotropin (PMSG; 300 IU, IM) were used to control oestrus in Female No. 2 (F2) beginning 22 September 1983 (Table 22.6). The timing and amount of prostaglandin (PG) and PMSG administered were based on recommendations made by Dr Barbara Durrant (San Diego Zoo). Because the stage of the oestrus cycle was known, only one injection of PG was given. Ovarian activity was monitored by analysing daily urine samples from F2 for pregnanediol-glucuronide (Figure 22.1).

231

Table 22.5: Information on the frozen semen samples which were evaluated using the bovine cervical mucus penetration test

Extender	Male	Collection Date	Subjective post-thaw motility (%)	Distance migrated (mm)
Lactose	M1	19 Sep 1980	30	37.5
	M2	7 Jan 1981	80	22.5
	M3	22 Jul 1980	50	23.0
	M4	7 Jan 1981	45	27.5
Raffinose	M1	4 Apr 1981	5	18.0
	M2	1 Apr 1981	5	10.5
	M3	14 Nov 1980	10	12.5
	M4	14 Nov 1980	1	17.5
Tris	M1	4 Apr 1981	55	32.0
	M1	29 May 1981	45	32.0
	M2	1 Apr 1981	50	31.0
	M2	29 Apr 1981	50	39.5
	M3	28 May 1981	50	24.5
	M3	28 May 1981	50 (straw)	22.0
	M4	28 May 1981	50	31.5

Regimen No. 2: The Synchro-mate-B system (Ceva Laboratories Inc., Overland Park, Kansas, USA) was used to control oestrus in Female No. 3 (F3), (Table 22.7). The standard Synchro-mate-B implant (6 mg norgestomet) and injection (5 mg estradiol valerate + 3 mg norgestomet) were used in the study.

Artificial Insemination

The AI procedure consisted of locating the cervix using a pyrex speculum (21.6 centimetres x 1.9 centimetres), positioning a stainless steel insemination pipette in the os cervix or anterior vagina, removing the speculum from the vagina and then depositing the frozen, thawed semen. Both females were manually restrained during the AI procedures. Because previous attempts to advance a pipette through the cervical rings had failed and because the cervix of the Addax is bifurcated at the level of the second or third cervical ring, no attempt was made to insert the insemination pipette past the os cervix. One millilitre of semen was inseminated on each day. When necessary, the volume of the frozen, thawed semen was reduced to 1 ml by centrifuging the sample for five minutes at

$450 \times$ g and drawing off the supernatant. Information on the semen samples used to A1 each female is presented in Table 22.8.

Table 22.6: Schedule of procedures for oestrus manipulation, artificial insemination (AI) and pregnancy diagnosis of F2

Date	Day	Procedure
12 Sep 1983	−13	Low serum progesterone (0.5 ng/ml) and urinary PdG (0.4 ng PdG/mg CR)
22 Sep 1983	− 3	PMSG (300 IU, IM)
24 Sep 1983	− 1	Prostaglandin (125 ug, IM) at 11.00 hrs
26 Sep 1983	1	AI at 11.00 hrs
27 Sep 1983	2	AI at 14.00 hrs
28 Sep 1983	3	AI at 14.30 hrs
29 Sep 1983	4	AI at 14.15 hrs

A total of 219×10^6 motile sperm inseminated (bracketed to AI entries above)

Date	Day	Procedure
18 Oct 1983	23	High serum progesterone (15.8 ng/ml) and urinary PdG (1.6 ng PdG/mg CR)
26 Oct 1983	31	High serum progesterone (10.1 ng/ml) and urinary PdG (1.6 ng PdG/mg CR)
3 Nov 1983	39	High serum progesterone (9.4 ng/ml) and urinary PdG (1.4 ng PdG/mg CR)
9 Nov 1983	45	Ultrasound examination: foetal heartbeat seen
18 Jun 1984	269	Calf born

233

Table 22.7: Schedule of procedures for oestrus manipulation, artifical insemination (AI) and pregnancy diagnosis of F3

Date	Day	Procedure
7 Sep 1984	−11	Synchro-mate implant and Synchro-mate injection
17 Sep 1984	− 1	Synchro-mate implant out at 07.00 hrs
19 Sep 1984	1	AI at 14.50 hrs ⎫ A total of 220×10^6
20 Sep 1984	2	AI at 12.20 hrs ⎬ motile sperm inseminated
1 Oct 1984	13	High serum progesterone (19.9 ng/ml)
9 Oct 1984	21	High serum progesterone (17.5 ng/ml)
17 Oct 1984	29	High serum progesterone (24.5 ng/ml)
30 Oct 1984	42	Ultrasound examination: foetal heartbeat seen
		No calf born

F2 gave birth to a normal male calf on 18 June 1984. The pregnancy of F3 was not carried to term.

Table 22.8: Information on the frozen, thawed semen used in the artificial insemination (AI) study

AI Date	Female	Male	Collection date	Extender	Count per pellet ($\times 10^6$)	Post-thaw motility (%)
26 Sep 83	F2	M3	28 May 81	Tris	26[a]	55–60
27 Sep 83	F2	M3	22 Jul 80	Lactose	3.0	50
28 Sep 83	F2	M3	22 Jul 80	Lactose	3.0	50
29 Sep 83	F2	M3	28 May 81	Tris	26[a]	40
19 Sep 84	F3	M1	21 Aug 80	Lactose	32.6[a]	40[b]
19 Sep 84	F3	M1	21 Aug 80	Lactose	67	40[b]
20 Sep 84	F3	M1	29 May 81	Tris	28.5	40

Notes: a. Straws.
b. Motility of combined semen.

Figure 22.1: Pregnanediol-glucuronide (PdG) immunoreactivity expressed per mg creatinine (CR) in urine samples collected from F2. The graph covers the period from 12 September (day −13) to 3 November (day 39). The days of prostaglandin injection (PG), PMSG injection, AI and blood sampling (B) are indicated by arrows. F2 was two years old in October 1983

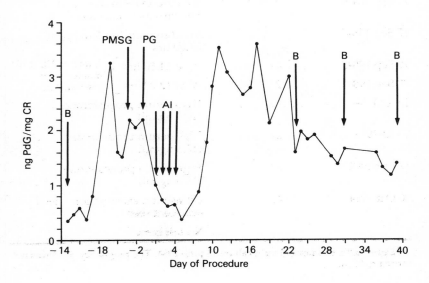

Day of Procedure

Pregnancy Diagnosis

Two methods of diagnosing pregnancy were used in this study. The first consisted of analysing the serum progesterone of three blood samples drawn at eight-day intervals, beginning a minimum of ten days after AI. The second method consisted of conducting an ultrasound examination 40–50 days after AI to verify pregnancy. The rectal probe used during the ultrasound examination was adapted for use in Addax by Bowen *et al.* (1987). The dates and results of the blood samples and ultrasound examinations are included in Tables 22.6 and 22.7

Acknowledgements

This study was made possible by F.W. 'Bert' Wheeler through his donation of the female and male Addax used in this research. The authors would also like to thank the following people for their assistance: Judy Friedl, John Pennycook, Gene Wiley and Naida Loskutoff. This project (15618–6143) was supported in part by the Texas Agricultural Experiment Station.

References

Bowen, J.M., Bergeron, H., DeBarros, C., and Kloppe, L. (1987) A modification of a 'real time' ultrasound probe used in the detection of pregnancy in minature horses and small ruminants. *Veterinary Medicine* (in press).

Densmore, M.A., and Kraemer, D.C. (1986) Analysis of reproductive data on the Addax (*Addax nasomaculatus*) in captivity. *Int. Zoo Ybk 24/25*: 303–6.

Densmore, M.A., Bowen, M.J., Magyar, S.J., Amoss, M.S. Jr., Robinson, R.M., Harms, P.G., and Kraemer, D.C. (1987a) Artificial insemination with frozen, thawed semen and pregnancy diagnosis in Addax (*Addax nasomaculatus*). *Zoo Biology 6* (1): 21–9.

Densmore, M.A., Bowen, M.J., Robinson, R.M., Harms, P.G., and Kraemer, D.C. (1987b). Haematologic and serum chemistry profiles of four male Addax (*Addax nasomaculatus*) immobilised with Etorphine and Xylazine. *Journal of Zoo Animal Medicine 18* (2/3): 123–30.

Densmore, M.A., Magyar, S.J., Amoss, M.S. Jr., Harms, P.G., Robinson, R.M., and Kraemer, D.C. (1987c) Analysis of reproductive parameters of male Addax (*Addax nasomaculatus*) in captivity. *Journal of Mammology*: submitted for publication.

Appendix

Normal haematological values of Hippotraginae (*data collected by C. Hawkey, Zoological Society of London, 1987*)

	Roan Antelope ($n = 10$)			Sable Antelope ($n = 6$)		
	Low	Mean	High	Low	Mean	High
Red cell count [$\times 10^{12}$/l]	10.32	14.07	17.81	10.54	15.30	20.06
White cell count [$\times 10^9$/l]	2.90	6.00	9.10	1.30	4.40	7.50
Haemoglobin [g/dl]	9.83	13.01	16.18	10.23	14.35	18.47
Packed cell volume [L/L]	27.10	34.70	42.30	27.90	36.30	44.80
Platelets [$\times 10^9$/l]	0.00	406.40	821.60	0.00	500.60	—
Reticulocytes	0.00	0.00	0.20	0.00	0.00	0.00
Mean cell volume [fl]	26.30	24.70	23.70	26.40	23.70	22.30
Mean cell haemoglobin [pg]	9.50	9.20	9.10	9.70	9.40	9.20
Mean cell haemoglobin concentrate [g/dl]	38.30	37.50	36.20	41.20	39.50	36.70
Erythrocyte sedimentation rate (wintrobes)	5.00	9.14	20.00	1.00	11.83	17.00
Heinz	0.00	0.33	2.00	0.00	0.00	0.00
Fibrinogen [g/l]	1.45	2.45	3.51	0.00	3.46	7.42
	Absolute values			*Absolute values*		
Neurophils [$\times 10^9$/l]	0.79	3.85	6.91	0.00	3.02	5.48
Lymphocytes [$\times 10^9$/l]	0.07	2.01	3.96	0.00	1.36	2.56
Monocytes [$\times 10^9$/l]	0.00	0.05	0.15	0.00	0.00	0.02
Eosinophils [$\times 10^9$/l]	0.00	0.00	0.00	0.00	0.00	0.00
Basophils [$\times 10^9$/l]	0.00	0.00	0.00	0.00	0.00	0.00

Normal haematological values of Hippotraginae (*data collected by C. Hawkey, Zoological Society of London, 1987*)

	Arabian Oryx (n = 6)			Scimitar-horned Oryx (n = 56)			Addax (n = 8)		
	Low	Mean	High	Low	Mean	High	Low	Mean	High
Red cell count [× 10¹²/l]	7.75	1.21	14.67	6.28	8.59	10.91	5.80	10.78	15.76
White cell count [×10⁹/l]	3.20	6.20	9.10	1.20	4.50	7.80	0.80	7.70	14.50
Haemoglobin [g/dl]	11.49	16.52	21.55	10.05	13.48	16.90	11.02	15.66	20.30
Packed cell volume [L/L]	31.00	44.50	58.00	29.80	38.40	47.00	28.90	43.10	57.30
Platelets [×10⁹/l]	0.00	263.60	696.30	0.00	303.70	656.00	143.80	204.30	264.70
Reticulocytes	0.00	0.00	0.00	0.00	0.20	3.30	0.00	0.00	0.10
Mean cell volume [fl]	40.00	39.70	39.50	47.50	44.70	43.10	49.90	40.00	36.40
Mean cell haemoglobin [pg]	14.80	14.70	14.70	16.00	15.70	15.50	19.00	14.50	12.90
Mean cell haemoglobin concentrate [g/dl]	37.20	37.10	37.00	36.00	35.10	33.70	35.40	36.30	38.10
Erythrocyte sedimentation rate (wintrobes)	0.00	0.50	2.00	0.00	3.49	13.00	0.50	5.64	15.00
Heinz	0.00	0.00	0.00	0.00	0.00	0.00	0.00	0.00	0.00
Fibrinogen [g/l]	1.26	2.62	3.98	1.50	2.66	3.82	2.04	2.87	3.71
	Absolute values			*Absolute values*			*Absolute values*		
Neutrophils [×10⁹/l]	2.09	4.58	7.07	0.38	3.07	5.76	3.64	4.16	7.40
Lymphocytes [×10⁹/l]	0.12	1.31	2.51	0.13	1.32	2.52	0.00	3.02	7.48
Monocytes [×10⁹/l]	0.00	0.10	0.22	0.00	0.03	0.11	0.09	0.21	0.66
Eosinophils [×10⁹/l]	0.07	0.00	0.00	0.00	0.00	0.00	0.09	0.00	0.00
Basophils [×10⁹/l]	0.00	0.00	0.00	0.00	0.00	0.00	0.00	0.00	0.00